DISCARD

D1603715

TOPOLOGY

An Outline for a First Course

PURE AND APPLIED MATHEMATICS

A Series of Monographs and Textbooks

COORDINATOR OF THE EDITORIAL BOARD

S. Kobayashi

UNIVERSITY OF CALIFORNIA AT BERKELEY

In Preparation:

TOPOLOGY

An Outline for a First Course

LEWIS E. WARD, Jr.

Mathematics Department
College of Liberal Arts
University of Oregon
Eugene, Oregon

MARCEL DEKKER, INC.   New York   1972

MARCEL DEKKER, INC.
95 Madison Avenue, New York, New York   10016

LIBRARY OF CONGRESS CATALOG CARD NUMBER: 70-76065

ISBN: 0-8247-1774-0

Current printing (last digit):

10   9   8   7   6   5   4   3   2

Printed in the United States of America

PREFACE

This volume is a textbook for a one-year, introductory course in topology. It is designed to be taught by the Socratic method, by which I mean that the instructor does not lecture in the ordinary sense, and the proofs of theorems are supplied by the students. It is appropriate for the instructor to discuss definitions and to provide such illustrative examples as he thinks necessary. But the proofs are to be devised by the students, and they are called upon to present their proofs in class. Ordinarily, the use of library materials is forbidden. Frequently his peers are a student's harshest critics, and in a successful class an atmosphere of friendly but intense competition is developed.

Beyond these simple groundrules, users of this teaching method employ many variations, especially as to the content of the course. It seems to me that the benefits of the method are largely independent of the topics to be covered. Obviously, a smaller segment of topology will be covered than in a conventional lecture course, at least during the initial months, so peripheral topics should not be emphasized unduly. The payoff for the sacrifice of extensive coverage of subject matter is the rapid development of deductive power on the part of the students. Such a course trains mathematicians at least as much as it teaches mathematics.

In my acquaintance, the mathematicians who teach topology by this Socratic method have nearly always developed their own courses over a period of years. Understandably, each is partial to the idiosyncracies of his own choice of subject matter. This being the case, why should one write such a book? The best answer I can supply is my hope that the book's existence will encourage others to try the method, using this book as a first approximation to their own future courses, and that a reasonable market can be found for such a missionary enterprise.

As noted above, the choice of topics to be covered is less important than the teaching method in a course of this sort. Nevertheless, a first course must ordinarily fulfill a service function in addition to the training of embryo topologists. For this reason I have included a large part of the material from general topology which has most utility in other branches of mathematics. Some standard topics have been omitted, most notably paracompact spaces, uniform spaces and function spaces. Hopefully, however, the student who completes this course will be prepared to go on either in topology or in other fields whose pursuit requires some topological background.

Because it is expected that student users of this book will devise their own proofs, none is included in the book. The course is nearly self-contained, the main prerequisites being a very modest acquaintance with set theory and the properties of the real numbers. A careful effort has been made to arrange the material so as to allow for the limitations of an undergraduate senior or first-year graduate student with no previous knowledge of topology. There are numerous examples, the details of which are usually omitted or provided in only the sparest form. Supplying those details is an important part of the course. Occasionally, when new concepts are introduced they are accompanied with some illustrative remarks, and hints are provided for the more difficult theorems, but these are the only departures from the format of definitions, theorems and examples without elaborative text. This is truly an _outline_ of a course in topology.

A brief word is in order concerning sources. I have bor-
rowed freely from a variety of primary and secondary sources,
including several standard textbooks. No effort has been made
to attribute theorems and concepts to their originators, except
that the names of mathematicians have been attached to a few
theorems where common usage dictates this. In keeping with the
spirit of self-discovery which is fundamental to the course,
there is no bibliography.

With some reluctance I have supplied an instructor's manual
in which proofs of the non-trivial theorems and details of the
more challenging examples are provided, though in rather cryptic
form. I applaud the instructor who chooses not to use the manual.
I applaud even more the instructor or student who concocts a
proof or devises an example more deft or elegant than those sug-
gested in the manual.

Eugene, Oregon   L. E. Ward, Jr.
March, 1972

CONTENTS

TOPOLOGY

An Outline for a First Course

0
PREREQUISITES

It is assumed that the reader has a modest familiarity with elementary set theory. Some notation and a few results, most of them not very deep, are recapitulated here.

The symbol

$$x \in S$$

is read "x <u>is</u> <u>an</u> <u>element</u> <u>of</u> <u>the</u> <u>set</u> S." The negation of this statement, "x <u>is</u> <u>not</u> <u>an</u> <u>element</u> <u>of</u> S," is written

$$x \notin S.$$

We write

$$A \subset B \quad \underline{or} \quad B \supset A$$

to mean that A is a <u>subset</u> of B. Two sets A and B are equal (A = B) provided A and B have precisely the same elements. If $A \subset B$ and $A \neq B$ then A is a <u>proper</u> subset of B.

The relation $\subset$ among sets is a <u>partial</u> <u>order</u>. That is, if A, B, and C are sets then

(0.1) $A \subset A$,

(0.2) if $A \subset B$ and $B \subset A$ then $A = B$,

(0.3) if $A \subset B$ and $B \subset C$ then $A \subset C$.

Suppose P is a property enjoyed by some (or all or none) of the elements in a set S. Then P defines a subset of S--namely, all the elements of S which have the property P. We write

$$\{x \in S : P(x)\}$$

to denote the <u>set</u> <u>of</u> <u>all</u> $x \in S$ <u>such</u> <u>that</u> x <u>has</u> <u>property</u> P. If no ambiguity is likely to occur, we may suppress the symbol S in this notation and write $\{x : P(x)\}$.

1

The <u>empty</u> <u>set</u>, denoted □, is defined by

$$\Box = \{x : x \neq x\},$$

the set which contains no elements. The empty set is a subset
of every set.

We distinguish between the object x and the set whose only
member is x. The latter is denoted $\{x\}$, sometimes called <u>sin</u>-
<u>gleton</u> x. This notation has a natural extension, so that $\{x, y\}$
is the set whose only members are x and y, and $\{a_1, a_2, \ldots, a_n\}$
is the set whose members are $a_1, a_2, \ldots, a_n$.

The <u>union</u> of two sets A and B, denoted $A \cup B$, is defined by

$$A \cup B = \{x : x \in A \ \underline{or} \ x \in B\}.$$

The <u>intersection</u> of two sets A and B, denoted $A \cap B$, is
defined by

$$A \cap B = \{x : x \in A \ \underline{and} \ x \in B\}.$$

More generally, if $\mathcal{A}$ is any family of sets then the <u>union</u>
of $\mathcal{A}$, denoted $\cup\mathcal{A}$, is defined by

$$\cup\mathcal{A} = \{x : x \in A \ \underline{for \ some} \ A \in \mathcal{A}\},$$

and if $\mathcal{A}$ is nonempty[1] then the <u>intersection</u> of $\mathcal{A}$, denoted $\cap\mathcal{A}$,
is defined by

$$\cap\mathcal{A} = \{x : x \in A \ \underline{for \ each} \ A \in \mathcal{A}\}.$$

If A and B are sets then A - B denotes the complement of B
relative to A, defined by

$$A - B = \{x : x \in A \ \underline{and} \ x \in B\}.$$

For brevity's sake the set A - B is sometimes called "A <u>minus</u> B."

The following results concerning operations on sets A, B,
and C are simple but useful.

(o.4) $A \cup B = B \cup A, \ A \cap B = B \cap A$;

(0.5) $A \cup (B \cup C) = (A \cup B) \cup C,$

         $A \cap (B \cap C) = (A \cap B) \cap C$;

(0.6) $A \cup (B \cap C) = (A \cup B) \cap (A \cup C),$

         $A \cap (B \cup C) = (A \cap B) \cup (A \cap C)$;

(0.7) $A = A \cup A = A \cap A$,

(0.8) $\square \cup A = A$, $\square \cap A = \square$.

(0.9)   These assertions are equivalent:

       $A \subset B$, $A \cap B = A$, $A \cup B = B$.

(0.10) If $A \subset S$ then $A \cup (S - A) = S$

       and $A \cap (S - A) = \square$.

If $\mathcal{A}$ is a family of sets and B is a set then

(0.11) $B \cap (\cup\mathcal{A}) = \cup \{B \cap A : A \in \mathcal{A}\}$.

       If $\mathcal{A} \neq \square$ then $B \cup (\cap\mathcal{A}) = \cap \{B \cup A : A \in \mathcal{A}\}$.

If $\mathcal{A}$ is a nonempty family of subsets of a set S then

(0.12) $S - \cup\mathcal{A} = \cap \{S - A : A \in \mathcal{A}\}$,

       $S - \cap\mathcal{A} = \cup \{S - A : A \in \mathcal{A}\}$.

    If A and B are sets then $A \times B$ is the set of all ordered pairs (a, b) where $a \in A$ and $b \in B$. The set $A \times B$ is called the Cartesian <u>product</u> of A and B or, briefly, the <u>product</u> of A and B.

(0.13) $(A \cup B) \times C = (A \times C) \cup (B \times C)$,

       $(A \cap B) \times C = (A \times C) \cap (B \times C)$;

(0.14) $A \times (B \cup C) = (A \times B) \cup (A \times C)$,

       $A \times (B \cap C) = (A \times B) \cap (A \times C)$;

(0.15) $(A \cap B) \times (C \cap D) = (A \times C) \cap (B \times D)$.

    As a matter of convenience we shall regard the sets $A \times (B \times C)$ and $(A \times B) \times C$ as being equal by identifying the element (a, (b, c)) of $A \times (B \times C)$ with the element ((a, b), c) of $(A \times B) \times C$. Consequently, the parentheses (in the product of a finite family of sets) become irrelevant and may be suppressed. If A_1, A_2, ..., A_n are sets then the elements of $A_1 \times A_2 \times \cdots \times A_n$ are written as ordered n-tuples $(a_1, a_2, ..., a_n)$ where $a_i \in A_i$ for each i = 1, 2, ..., n.

    If A and B are sets a <u>relation</u> between A and B is a set, $\mathcal{R} \subset A \times B$. If $(a, b) \in \mathcal{R}$ one sometimes writes $a\mathcal{R}b$. A relation between A and A is called a relation <u>on</u> A.

A <u>partial</u> <u>order</u> on a set S is a relation Γ on S which
satisfies these laws:

(0.16) If $x \in S$ then $(x, x) \in \Gamma$.

(0.17) If $(x, y) \in \Gamma$ and $(y, x) \in \Gamma$ then $x = y$.

(0.18) If $(x, y) \in \Gamma$ and $(y, z) \in \Gamma$ then $(x, z) \in \Gamma$.

If Γ is a partial order it is common to write $x \leq y$ as a synonym
for $(x, y) \in \Gamma$. With this notation the laws (0.16)-(0.18)
become

(0.16') If $x \in S$ then $x \leq x$.

(0.17') If $x \leq y$ and $y \leq x$ then $x = y$.

(0.18') If $x \leq y$ and $y \leq z$ then $x \leq z$.

The symbol $x < y$ means that $x \leq y$ but $x \neq y$. The following
rules for $<$ are easy to verify:

(0.19) If $x \in S$ then $x < x$ cannot occur.

(0.20) If $x < y$ and $y < z$ then $x < z$.

A relation Γ on a set S is an <u>order</u> <u>relation</u> if it is a partial
order which satisfies the further law:

(0.21) If $(x, y) \in S \times S$ then $(x, y) \in \Gamma$ or $(y, x) \in \Gamma$.

An order relation is also called an <u>order</u>, a <u>simple</u> <u>order</u>, or a
<u>linear</u> <u>order</u>.

If (S, Γ) is a partially ordered set and if C is a subset
of S such that $\Gamma \cap (C \times C)$ is a simple order, then C is a <u>chain</u>
of S.

If S is an ordered set, $A \subset S$, and if $x_1 \in S$ such that
$a \leq x_1$ for each $a \in A$, then x_1 is an <u>upper</u> <u>bound</u> of A. If
$x_0 \in S$ and $x_0 \leq a$ for each $a \in A$, then x_0 is a <u>lower</u> <u>bound</u> of A.
If the set of upper bounds of A has a least member (i. e., an
upper bound which precedes all other upper bounds), then it is
the <u>least</u> <u>upper</u> <u>bound</u> of A, abbreviated l. u. b. A. The <u>greatest</u>
<u>lower</u> <u>bound</u> of A, abbreviated g. l. b. A, is defined dually.

Obviously every subset of an ordered (partially ordered)
set is ordered (partially ordered) with respect to the same
relation.[2]

We reserve the symbol $\underset{\sim}{R}$ to denote the ordered set of real numbers, and it is assumed that the reader is familiar with the elementary properties of $\underset{\sim}{R}.$[3] We write

$$\underset{\sim}{R}^2 = \underset{\sim}{R} \times \underset{\sim}{R}$$

to denote <u>Euclidean 2-space</u>, the set of all ordered pairs of real numbers, and

$$\underset{\sim}{R}^n = \underbrace{\underset{\sim}{R} \times \underset{\sim}{R} \times \cdots \times \underset{\sim}{R}}_{n \quad \text{factors}}$$

to denote <u>Euclidean n-space</u>, the set of all ordered n-tuples of real numbers. The symbols $\underset{\sim}{Q}$, $\underset{\sim}{Z}$, and $\underset{\sim}{N}$ are reserved to denote the sets of **rational** numbers, **integers**, and **natural** numbers, respectively.

If S is an ordered set (and in particular, if $S = \underset{\sim}{R}$) and if a, b $\in$ S such that a < b, then we write

$]a, b[= \{x \in S : a < x < b\},$

$]a, b] = \{x \in S : a < x \leq b\},$

$[a, b[= \{x \in S : a \leq x < b\},$

$[a, b] = \{x \in S : a \leq x \leq b\},$

$]a, \infty[= \{x \in S : a < x\},$

$[a, \infty[= \{x \in S : a \leq x\},$

$]-\infty, b[= \{x \in S : x < b\},$

$]-\infty, b] = \{x \in S : x \leq b\}.$

In the ordered set $\underset{\sim}{R}$ we reserve the symbol I to denote the set [0,1]. Further, we write

$$I^2 = \{(x, y) \in \underset{\sim}{R}^2 : 0 \leq x, y \leq 1\},$$

$$I^n = \{(x_1, \ldots, x_n) \in \underset{\sim}{R}^n : 0 \leq x_i \leq 1\}.$$

An <u>equivalence relation</u> on a set S is a relation δ on S which satisfies the following laws.

(0.22) If $x \in S$ then $(x, x) \in \delta$.

(0.23) If $(x, y) \in \delta$ then $(y, x) \in \delta$.

(0.24) If $(x, y) \in \delta$ and $(y, z) \in \delta$ then $(x, z) \in \delta$.

We have

(0.25)   A relation $\mathcal{S}$ on a set S is an equivalence relation
on S if and only if there exists a family $\mathcal{Q}$ of mutually disjoint
sets such that (i) $\cup \mathcal{Q}$ = S and (ii) (x, y) $\in \mathcal{S}$ if and only if
there exists A $\in \mathcal{Q}$ such that x, y $\in$ A.

The members of $\mathcal{Q}$ are called equivalence classes of $\mathcal{S}$.

If X and Y are sets then a relation f between X and Y is
called a function if, for each x $\in$ X, there exists a unique
element f(x) $\in$ Y such that (x, f(x)) $\in$ f. The set X is called
the domain of the function f and we write

$$f : X \rightarrow Y,$$

which is read "f is a function on (or, from) X into Y."

If A $\subset$ X we write

$$f(A) = \{f(x) : x \in A\}.$$

This set is the image of A under f. The image of the domain of
a function is the range of the function. If f : X $\rightarrow$ Y and if
Y is the range of f then f is said to be a surjection or to be
surjective.

If B $\subset$ Y then

$$f^{-1}(B) = \{x \in X : f(x) \in B\}$$

is the inverse image of B under f.

If A $\subset$ X then a new function f$|$A (read "f restricted to A")
is given by the formula

$$(f|A)(x) = f(x)$$

for each x $\in$ A. Thus f$|$A is a function from A into Y.

If f : X $\rightarrow$ Y and g : Y $\rightarrow$ Z are functions then the composition
of f by g, denoted gf : X $\rightarrow$ Z, is defined by

$$(gf)(x) = g(f(x)).$$

It is obvious that the composition of f by g is a function.

A function f : X $\rightarrow$ Y is an injection provided $f^{-1}(y)$ contains at most one element, for each y $\in$ Y. A function which is

an injection is said to be <u>injective</u> or <u>one-to-one</u>. An injective
surmorphism is called a <u>bijection</u> and is said to be <u>bijective</u>.
Clearly, if f is injective then $f^{-1} : f(X) \to X$ is a bijection.
The property of being injective is preserved by restrictions
and compositions. The property of being bijective is preserved
by compositions.

The following assertions are valid where $f : X \to Y$ is a
function, $A \subset X$, $B \subset Y$, and $\mathcal{A}$ and $\mathcal{B}$ are nonempty families of
subsets of X and Y, respectively.

(0.26) $f(\cup\mathcal{A}) = \cup \{f(A) : A \in \mathcal{A}\}$

(0.27) $f(\cap\mathcal{A}) \subset \cap \{f(A) : A \in \mathcal{A}\}$

(0.28) $f^{-1}(\cup\mathcal{B}) = \cup \{f^{-1}(B) : B \in \mathcal{B}\}$

(0.29) $f^{-1}(\cap\mathcal{B}) = \cap \{f^{-1}(B) : B \in \mathcal{B}\}$

(0.30) $A \subset f^{-1} f(A)$

(0.31) $ff^{-1}(B) = B \cap f(X)$.

If f is injective then the inclusions (0.27) and (0.30) become
equalities.

If A and B are sets and there exists a bijection from A
onto B, then A and B are said to have the same <u>cardinal number</u>.
We write $\#(A)$ to denote the cardinal number of the set A and we
identify the finite cardinal numbers with the natural numbers
0, 1, 2, ... We assume some familiarity with the cardinal num-
bers. We write $\aleph_0 = \#(\underset{\sim}{N})$, $c = \#(\underset{\sim}{R})$; then $2^{\aleph_0} = c$ where $2^{\aleph_0}$
is the cardinal number of the set of all subsets of $\underset{\sim}{N}$. If a and
b are cardinal numbers and if A and B are sets such that
$\#(A) = a$ and $\#(B) = b$, we write $a \leq b$ provided there is an injection from A into B. The relation $\leq$ on cardinal numbers is
an order relation. (This last fact is far from trivial.)

A set S is <u>well ordered</u> by the relation $\leq$ [or $(S, \leq)$ is a
<u>well ordered</u> set] provided $(S, \leq)$ is an ordered set and, if T
is a nonempty subset of S, then T has an initial element, i. e.,
there exists $t_0 \in T$ such that $t_0 \leq t$ for all $t \in T$. Clearly

($\underset{\sim}{N}$, $\leq$) is well ordered but ($\underset{\sim}{R}$, $\leq$) is not. The following basic
principle is assumed as an axiom.

Well-Ordering Principle. Every set can be well ordered.

The two statements which follow are each logically equivalent to the well-ordering principle.

Axiom of Choice. If $\mathcal{Q}$ is a family of nonempty sets then
there exists a function $c : \mathcal{Q} \rightarrow \cup \mathcal{Q}$ such that $c(A) \in A$ for each
$A \in \mathcal{Q}$.

Hausdorff Maximality Principle. If P is a partially ordered
set then P contains a maximal chain, i. e., a chain which is
properly contained in no other chain of P.

If S is a set, then a function $m : S \times S \rightarrow S$ is an **operation**
on S. We write $m(x, y) = xy$, $m(\{x\} \times A) = xA$, $m(A \times \{x\}) = Ax$,
and $m(A \times B) = AB$, where $x, y \in S$ and A and B are subsets of S.

A **group** is a pair (G, m) where G is a set and m is an operation on G such that $x(yz) = (xy)z$ and $xG = G = Gx$, for all
$x, y, z \in G$. Standard examples of groups are ($\underset{\sim}{R}$, +), ($\underset{\sim}{Q}$, +),
and (S^1, $\cdot$), where S^1 denotes the set of complex numbers of
modulus one and $\cdot$ denotes multiplication of complex numbers.

If (G, m) and (H, μ) are groups, then a function $h : G \rightarrow H$
is a **homomorphism** if $h(xy) = h(x)h(y)$, for each $x, y \in G$. An
injective homomorphism is an **isomorphism**. If h is a surjective
isomorphism, we write (G, m) $\cong$ (H, μ).

If (G, m) and (H, μ) are groups, then the pair (G $\times$ H, λ)
is a group, where

$$\lambda((g_1, h_1), (g_2, h_2)) = (m(g_1, g_2), \mu(h_1, h_2)).$$

FOOTNOTES

(1)According to the definition, $\cup \square$ is simply the empty set, but the definition of $\cap \square$ introduces difficulties which are peripheral to the purposes of this volume. Accordingly, we eschew altogether the intersection of the empty family.

(2)More precisely, if Γ is an order (partial order) on the set S and if $T \subset S$ then $\Gamma \cap (T \times T)$ is an order (partial order) on T.

(3)That is, $\underset{\sim}{R}$, together with the operations of addition and multiplication, is a complete ordered field and the resulting arithmetic consequences.

1
TOPOLOGICAL SPACES

Definition. A <u>topological space</u> is a pair (X, $\mathcal{J}$) where X is a nonempty set and $\mathcal{J}$ is a family of subsets of X satisfying these rules:

    (i) $\square \in \mathcal{J}$ and X $\in \mathcal{J}$;

    (ii) if $\mathcal{A} \subset \mathcal{J}$ then $\cup \mathcal{A} \in \mathcal{J}$;

    (iii) if $\mathcal{A} \subset \mathcal{J}$ and $\mathcal{A}$ is finite then $\cap \mathcal{A} \in \mathcal{J}$.

The members of $\mathcal{J}$ are called <u>open sets</u> and the family $\mathcal{J}$ is the <u>topology</u> of the space (X, $\mathcal{J}$). If U $\in \mathcal{J}$ then X - U is called a <u>closed set</u>.

Examples.

(1) Let X be any nonempty set and let $\mathcal{J}$ be the family of all subsets of X. Then every subset of X is both open and closed. Such topological spaces are called <u>discrete</u>.

(2) Let X be any nonempty set and let $\mathcal{J} = \{\square, X\}$. The sets $\square$ and X are the only open sets. They are also the only closed sets. Whereas discrete spaces have the largest possible topology, these spaces have the smallest possible topology. We term these topological spaces <u>indiscrete</u>.

(3) Let X be any nonempty set and let $\mathcal{J}$ denote the family of all subsets A of X such that A = $\square$ or X - A is finite. Except for $\square$, the open sets are simply the complements of finite sets. Accordingly, (X, $\mathcal{J}$) is called a <u>cofinite space</u>.

(4) If t $\in \underset{\sim}{R}$, the set of real numbers, and $\varepsilon \in \underset{\sim}{R}$ with $\varepsilon > 0$, let S(t, ε) = $\{x \in \underset{\sim}{R} : |x - t| < \varepsilon\}$. Call a subset of $\underset{\sim}{R}$ <u>open</u> if it is the union of sets S(t, ε). The open sets yield a

topology called the Euclidean topology for $\underset{\sim}{R}$. Unless the contrary is specifically stated, the Euclidean topology is tacitly
assumed whenever $\underset{\sim}{R}$ is regarded as a topological space.

(5) If $t = (t_1, \ldots, t_n) \in \underset{\sim}{R}^n$ and if $\varepsilon > 0$, let $S(t, \varepsilon) =$
$\{x \in \underset{\sim}{R}^n : \Sigma_{i=1}^n |x_i - t_i|^2 < \varepsilon^2\}$, the sphere about t of radius ε.
Call a set open if it is the union of such spheres. This yields
the Euclidean topology for $\underset{\sim}{R}^n$. As in the preceeding example,
the Euclidean topology is always presumed unless the contrary is
stated.

(6) Let X be a nonempty set and let $\mathcal{B}$ be a family of subsets of X. If $\mathcal{T}(\mathcal{B})$ denotes the intersection of all topologies
on X which contain $\mathcal{B}$ as a subfamily, then $\mathcal{T}(\mathcal{B})$ is a topology on
X, called the topology generated by $\mathcal{B}$.

(7) The discrete topology is generated by the singleton
sets.

(8) The indiscrete topology is generated by the empty
family.

(9) The Euclidean topology on $\underset{\sim}{R}$ is generated by the family
of all rays $]a, \infty[$ and $]-\infty, b[$.

For the sake of brevity we shall often say "space" where
"topological space" is meant. Thus we will write "the space X"
instead of "the topological space $(X, \mathcal{T})$."

Theorem 1. If X is a space and if $\mathcal{F}$ is the family of all
closed subsets of X then

(i) $\square \in \mathcal{F}$ and $X \in \mathcal{F}$,

(ii) if $\mathcal{A} \subset \mathcal{F}$ then $\cap \mathcal{A} \in \mathcal{F}$,

(iii) if $\mathcal{A} \subset \mathcal{F}$ and $\mathcal{A}$ is finite then $\cup \mathcal{A} \in \mathcal{F}$.

Definition. Let X be a space and $p \in X$. If N is a subset
of X such that $p \in U \subset N$ for some open set U, then N is a neighborhood of p.

Theorem 2. Let X be a space and $p \in X$. If N_1 and N_2 are neighborhoods of p then $N_1 \cap N_2$ is a neighborhood of p. If N is a neighborhood of p and $N \subset M \subset X$ then M is a neighborhood of p. A subset of X is open if and only if it is a neighborhood of each of its elements.

Definition. If X is a space and $A \subset X$ then
$$\overline{A} = \{x \in X : \text{if N is a neighborhood of x then } N \cap A \neq \square\}.$$
The set $\overline{A}$ is called the closure of A.

Examples.

(10) In any space, $\overline{\square} = \square$ and $\overline{X} = X$.

(11) In a discrete space, $\overline{A} = A$ for all subsets A.

(12) If X is an indiscrete space and A is a nonempty sub-set of X, then $\overline{A} = X$.

(13) If X is a cofinite space and A is a finite subset, then $\overline{A} = A$, but if A is an infinite subset then $\overline{A} = X$.

Proposition 1.1. If $t \in \mathbb{R}$ then a subset N of $\mathbb{R}$ is a neighborhood of t if and only if there exists a, $b \in \mathbb{R}$ with $t \in]a, b[\subset N$. If $x \in \mathbb{R}^n$ then a subset M of $\mathbb{R}^n$ is a neighborhood of x if and only if x is an element of a sphere contained in M.

Examples.

(14) In the space $\mathbb{R}$, $\overline{]0, 1[} = \overline{]0, 1]} = \overline{[0, 1[} = \overline{[0, 1]} = [0, 1]$ and $\overline{]0, \infty[} = \overline{[0, \infty[} = [0, \infty[$. Moreover, $\overline{\mathbb{Q}} = \overline{\mathbb{R} - \mathbb{Q}} = \mathbb{R}$ and $\overline{\mathbb{Z}} = \mathbb{Z}$.

(15) In the space $\mathbb{R}^2$ suppose T is the triangle consisting of the line segments joining (0, 0) and (0, 1), (0, 0) and (1, 0), and (0, 1) and (1, 0). If $J = \{(x, y) \in \mathbb{R}^2 : 0 < x, y ; x + y < 1\}$ and if $J \subset A \subset J \cup T$, then $\overline{A} = J \cup T$. Moreover, $\overline{\mathbb{Q} \times \mathbb{Q}} = \overline{\mathbb{Q} \times (\mathbb{R} - \mathbb{Q})} = \mathbb{R}^2$ and $\overline{\mathbb{Z} \times \mathbb{Z}} = \mathbb{Z} \times \mathbb{Z}$.

Theorem 3. If X is a space and A and B are subsets of X
then

(i) $A \subset \overline{A}$,

(ii)   if $A \subset B$ then $\overline{A} \subset \overline{B}$,

(iii) $\overline{A} = \cap \{F : A \subset F$ and F is a closed set$\}$,

(iv)   A is closed if and only if $\overline{A} = A$,

(v) $\overline{A} = \overline{\overline{A}}$,

(vi) $\overline{A \cup B} = \overline{A} \cup \overline{B}$.

Theorem 3 is a catalog of properties of the closure operator.
A natural question is whether some of the items in that catalog
actually characterize the closure operator. The answer is
spelled out precisely in Theorem 4.

Definition. Let S be a nonempty set and suppose k is a
function which assigns to each subset A of S another subset $k(A)$
subject to the conditions:

(K1)   if $A \subset S$ then $A \subset k(A)$,

(K2) $k(\square) = \square$,

(K3)   if $A, B \subset S$ then $k(A \cup B) = k(A) \cup k(B)$,

(K4)   if $A \subset S$ then $k(k(A)) \subset k(A)$.

Then k is called a Kuratowski closure operator for S.

Theorem 4. If S is a nonempty set and k is a Kuratowski
closure operator for S let
$$\mathcal{J}(k) = \{U \subset S : k(S - U) = S - U\}.$$
Then $(S, \mathcal{J}(k))$ is a topological space and $k(A) = \overline{A}$ for each $A \subset S$.

Definition. If X is a space and $A \subset X$, then
$A^\circ = \{x \in X : N \subset A$ for some neighborhood N of x$\}$;
the set A° is called the interior of A.

Examples.

(16)   In any space X, $\square^\circ = \square$ and $X^\circ = X$.

(17)   In a discrete space, $A^\circ = A$ for all subsets A.

(18) In an indiscrete space, $A^o = \Box$ for all proper subsets A.

(19) In a cofinite space, $A^o = \Box$ if A has infinite complement, and $A^o = A$ if A has finite complement.

(20) In the space $\underset{\sim}{R}$, $]0, 1[=]0, 1[^o =]0, 1]^o = [0, 1[^o = [0, 1]^o$ and $]0, \infty[=]0, \infty[^o = [0, \infty[^o$; further, $\underset{\sim}{Q}^o = (\underset{\sim}{R} - \underset{\sim}{Q})^o = \Box$.

(21) In the space $\underset{\sim}{R}^2$ let T and J be defined as in Example 15. If $J \subset A \subset (J \cup P)$ then $A^o = J$.

Theorem 5. If X is a space and $A \subset X$, then
(i) $A^o = X - \overline{X - A}$ and $\overline{A} = X - (X - A)^o$.
Consequently, if $B \subset X$ then
(ii) $A^o \subset A$,
(iii) if $A \subset B$ then $A^o \subset B^o$,
(iv) $A^o = \cup \{U : U \text{ is open and } U \subset A\}$,
(v) A is open if and only if $A = A^o$,
(vi) $A^o = A^{oo}$,
(vii) $(A \cap B)^o = A^o \cap B^o$.

Definition. If X is a space and $A \subset X$ then the boundary of A, denoted ∂A, is defined by
$$\partial A = \overline{A} \cap \overline{X - A}.$$

Examples.
(22) In any space X, $\partial \Box = \partial X = \Box$.
(23) In a discrete space, $\partial A = \Box$ for all subsets A.
(24) In an indiscrete space X, $\partial A = X$ for each proper nonempty subset A.
(25) If X is an infinite cofinite space then $\partial A = A$ if A is a finite subset, $\partial A = X - A$ if $X - A$ is finite, and $\partial A = X$ if A and $X - A$ are both infinite.
(26) In the space $\underset{\sim}{R}$, $\partial]0, 1[= \partial [0, 1[= \partial]0, 1] = \partial [0, 1] = \{0, 1\}$. Moreover, $\partial \underset{\sim}{Q} = \partial (\underset{\sim}{R} - \underset{\sim}{Q}) = \underset{\sim}{R}$ and $\partial \underset{\sim}{Z} = \underset{\sim}{Z}$.

Proposition 1.2. If X is a space and A ⊂ X, then ∂A = □ if and only if A is both open and closed.

Theorem 6. If X is a space and A and B are subsets of X, then

  (i)   ∂A = ∂(X - A),
  (ii) ∂A = $\overline{A}$ - A°,
  (iii) $\overline{A}$ = A ∪ ∂A,
  (iv) A° = A - ∂A,
  (v)   ∂(∂A) ⊂ ∂A,
  (vi) A ∩ B ∩ ∂(A ∩ B) = A ∩ B ∩ (∂A ∪ ∂B).

It is a useful device to conceive of $\underset{\sim}{R}$ as a subset of $\underset{\sim}{R}^2$ by identifying each t ∈ $\underset{\sim}{R}$ with the element (t, 0) ∈ $\underset{\sim}{R}^2$, i. e., $\underset{\sim}{R}$ is identified with the x axis in $\underset{\sim}{R}^2$. This device is especially useful in topology because each open subset of $\underset{\sim}{R}^2$, when intersected with the x axis, yields an open subset of $\underset{\sim}{R}$ under the identification. Conversely, each open subset of $\underset{\sim}{R}$ is the intersection of $\underset{\sim}{R}$ with a suitably chosen open subset of $\underset{\sim}{R}^2$. Thus we may regard $\underset{\sim}{R}$ as a subspace of $\underset{\sim}{R}^2$. This suggests that any subset of a topological space can be made into another space by defining the topology of the subspace in an analogous fashion.

Theorem 7. If (X, $\mathcal{J}$) is a space and Y is a nonempty subset of X, define

$$\mathcal{J}(Y) = \{U \cap Y : U \in \mathcal{J}\}.$$

Then (Y, $\mathcal{J}(Y)$) is a space and a subset P of Y is open (closed) with respect to $\mathcal{J}(Y)$ if and only if there exists Q ⊂ X such that Q is open (closed) with respect to $\mathcal{J}$ and P = Q ∩ Y.

Definition. If (X, $\mathcal{J}$) is a space and Y is a nonempty subset of X, then $\mathcal{J}(Y)$ is called the relative topology of Y. The space (Y, $\mathcal{J}(Y)$) is a subspace of (X, $\mathcal{J}$).

Example.

(27) Every subspace of a discrete (indiscrete, cofinite) space is discrete (indiscrete, cofinite).

Theorem 8. Let $(X, \mathcal{J})$ be a space and suppose $A \subset Y \subset X$ with $Y \neq \square$. If $\mathcal{C}\ell(A, Y)$ denotes the closure of A relative to $\mathcal{J}(Y)$ then $\mathcal{C}\ell(A, Y) = \overline{A} \cap Y$. If $x \in Y$ then the neighborhoods of x relative to $\mathcal{J}(Y)$ are precisely the sets $N_x \cap Y$, where N_x is a neighborhood of x relative to $\mathcal{J}$.

Definition. Let $(X, \mathcal{J})$ be a space and suppose $\mathcal{B}$ is a subfamily of $\mathcal{J}$ with the property that each open subset of X is the union of members of $\mathcal{B}$. Then $\mathcal{B}$ is called a base for $\mathcal{J}$.

Obviously, if $\mathcal{B}$ is a base for $\mathcal{J}$ then $\mathcal{J} = \mathcal{J}(\mathcal{B})$.

Example.

(28) If X is a nonempty set then $\{\{x\} : x \in X\}$ is a base for the discrete topology on X and $\{X\}$ is a base for the indiscrete topology.

Proposition 1.3. In the space $\underset{\sim}{R}$ the family of all intervals $]a, b[$ where $a < b$ and a and b are rational numbers, is a base for the Euclidean topology. In the space $\underset{\sim}{R}^n$ the family of all spheres $S(t, 1/m)$, where t has rational coordinates and $m = 1, 2, \ldots$, is a base for the Euclidean topology.

Example.

(29) Let $a_1, \ldots, a_n, b_1, \ldots, b_n$ be rational numbers with $a_i < b_i$ for each $i = 1, \ldots, n$, and let
$$B(a, b) = \{x \in \underset{\sim}{R}^n : a_i < x_i < b_i; i = 1, \ldots, n\}.$$
Then the set of all $B(a, b)$ is a base for the Euclidean topology on $\underset{\sim}{R}^n$.

Proposition 1.4. If $(X, \mathcal{J})$ is a space, $\mathcal{B}$ is a base for $\mathcal{J}$, and Y is a nonempty subset of X, then $\{B \cap Y : B \in \mathcal{B}\}$ is a base for $\mathcal{J}(Y)$.

Theorem 9. If $(X, \mathcal{J})$ is a space and $\mathcal{B}$ is a base for $\mathcal{J}$, then (i) $\cup \mathcal{B} = X$ and (ii) if $x \in X$ and if B_1, $B_2 \in \mathcal{B}$ such that $x \in B_1 \cap B_2$, then there exists $B_3 \in \mathcal{B}$ such that $x \in B_3 \subset B_1 \cap B_2$. Conversely, if $\mathcal{B}$ is a family of sets satisfying (i) and (ii) then $\mathcal{B}$ is a base for $\mathcal{J}(\mathcal{B})$.

Corollary 9.1. If X is a set, $\mathcal{A}$ is a family of subsets of X, and $\mathcal{B}$ is the family of intersections of nonempty, finite sub-families of $\mathcal{A}$, then $\{X\} \cup \mathcal{B}$ is a base for $\mathcal{J}(\mathcal{A})$.

Definition. Let M be a nonempty set. A _metric_ for M is a function $\rho : M \times M \to \underset{\sim}{R}$ satisfying

(Mi) $\rho \geq 0$ and $\rho(x, y) = 0$ if and only if $x = y$,

(M2) $\rho(x, y) = \rho(y, x)$ for all x, y $\in$ M,

(M3) if x, y, z $\in$ M then $\rho(x, z) \leq \rho(x, y) + \rho(y, z)$.

If ρ is a metric for M then (M, ρ) is a _metric space_. If $\epsilon > 0$ and $x \in M$, then

$$S(x, \epsilon) = \{y \in M : \rho(x, y) < \epsilon\}$$

is the (_open_) _sphere_ with _center_ x and _radius_ ϵ. It is readily seen that the family of all such spheres is a base for a topology on M which is called the _metric topology_, or the _topology generated_ by ρ, or the ρ _topology_. A topological space is _metrizable_ if its topology is generated by some metric.

Examples.

(30) With $M \neq \Box$, let $\rho(x, y) = 1$ if x, y $\in$ M and x $\neq$ y, and let $\rho(x, x) = 0$. Then (M, ρ) is a metric space and the metric topology is discrete. Consequently, every discrete space is metrizable.

(31) Define ρ on $\underset{\sim}{R} \times \underset{\sim}{R}$ by $\rho(x, y) = |x - y|$. Then ρ is a metric and so $\underset{\sim}{R}$ is metrizable.

(32)   Define ρ on $\underset{\sim}{R}^n \times \underset{\sim}{R}^n$ by $\rho(x, y) = \Sigma_{i=1}^n |x_i - y_i|^2)^{1/2}$.
Then ρ is a metric for $\underset{\sim}{R}^n$ and so $\underset{\sim}{R}^n$ is metrizable.

(33)   An indiscrete space containing more than one element
is not metrizable.

(34)   An infinite cofinite space is not metrizable.

(35)   Define $\sigma : \underset{\sim}{R}^n \times \underset{\sim}{R}^n \to \underset{\sim}{R}$ by $\sigma(x, y) = \Sigma_{i=1}^n |x_i - y_i|$.
Then σ is a metric and the σ topology is the Euclidean topology.

Theorem 10.   If (M, ρ) is a metric space then a subset of
M is open if and only if it is the union of open spheres.   If U
is an open subset of M and $x \in U$, then there exists $\epsilon > 0$ such
that $S(x, \epsilon) \subset U$.   If T is a subset of M and $\epsilon > 0$, then
$$T_\epsilon = \{x \in M : \rho(x, t) < \epsilon \text{ for some } t \in T\}$$
is an open set.   Each open subset of M is the union of a countable family of closed sets, and each closed subset of M is the
intersection of a countable family of open sets.   If $A \subset M$ then
$$\overline{A} = \{x \in M : \text{ if } \epsilon > 0 \text{ then there exists}$$
$$a \in A \text{ such that } \rho(x, a) < \epsilon\},$$
$$A^O = \{x \in M : \text{ there exists } \epsilon > 0 \text{ such that}$$
$$S(x, \epsilon) \subset A\},$$
and
$$\partial A = \{x \in M : \text{ if } \epsilon > 0 \text{ then there exists}$$
$$a \in A \text{ and } b \in M - A \text{ such that}$$
$$\rho(x, a) < \epsilon \text{ and } \rho(x, b) < \epsilon\}.$$
Finally, if $\square \neq N \subset M$ and $\rho_N = \rho|(N \times N)$, then (N, ρ_N) is a
metric space and the ρ_N topology is the relative topology.

Example.

(36)   If (M, ρ) is a metric space, $x \in M$, and $\epsilon > 0$, then
$\{y \in M : \rho(x, y) \leq \epsilon\}$ is a closed set which is not, in general,
the same as $\overline{S(x, \epsilon)}$.

Definition.   A sequence is a function whose domain is the
set $\underset{\sim}{N}$.   If x is a sequence whose range is contained in a set S

then x is a sequence _in_ S. It is customary to write x_0 = x(0),
x_1 = x(1), ..., x_n = x(n), etc. If x is a sequence and y is a
sequence in $\underset{\sim}{N}$ such that $y_{n+1} > y_n$ for each n $\in \underset{\sim}{N}$, then the
composition xy is a _subsequence_ of x. A sequence x is _eventually_
in the set T if there exists n(T) $\in \underset{\sim}{N}$ such that $x_n \in$ T for all
n > n(T), and x is _frequently_ in T if for each n $\in \underset{\sim}{N}$ there exists
m > n such that $x_m \in$ T. If x is a sequence in a space X then x
converges to the element p $\in$ X provided x is eventually in every
neighborhood of p, and x _clusters_ to p provided x is frequently
in every neighborhood of p. If x converges to p we write
$$\lim x = p, \text{ or } \lim_{n \to \infty} x_n = p, \text{ or } x_n \to p,$$
and we say that p is the _limit_ of the sequence x. If x clusters
to p then p is a _cluster point_ of x.

Examples.

(37) In the space $\underset{\sim}{R}$ the sequence 1/n converges to 0. The
sequence x_{2n} = 0, x_{2n+1} = 1 does not converge, but it clusters
to 0 and 1. If y_n = 2n then xy is constant and converges to 0.
The sequence x_n = n does not converge and does not cluster.

(38) A sequence in a discrete space converges (clusters)
if and only if it is eventually (frequently) constant.

(39) A sequence in an indiscrete space converges to every
element of the space.

(40) In a cofinite space, injective sequences converge to
every element. Sequences which are not frequently constant
cluster to every element.

Proposition 1.5. A sequence is frequently in a set T if
and only if some subsequence is eventually in T. Consequently,
if x is a sequence in a metric space, then x clusters to p if
and only if some subsequence of x converges to p.

Theorem 11. Let (M, ρ) be a metric space. If A $\subset$ M then
x $\in \overline{A}$ if and only if some sequence in A converges to x. A subset

U of M is open if and only if each sequence which converges to
an element of U is eventually in U.

Definition. If (M, ρ) is a metric space and $\square \neq A \subset M$,
then the diameter of A is defined by
$$\text{diam}(A) = 1. \text{ u. b. } \{\rho(x, y) : x, y \in A\},$$
and $\text{diam}(\square) = 0$.

Example.

(41) In the discrete metric space of Example 30 every
nondegenerate[1] set has diameter 1. A subset of R has finite
diameter if and only if it lies in an interval.

Theorem 12. If A and B are subsets of a metric space then
(i) $\text{diam}(A) = 0$ if and only if $\#(A) \leq 1$,
(ii) if $A \subset B$ then $\text{diam}(A) \leq \text{diam}(B)$,
(iii) $\text{diam}(\overline{A}) = \text{diam}(A)$,
(iv) if $A \cap B \neq \square$ then $\text{diam}(A \cup B) \leq \text{diam}(A) + \text{diam}(B)$.

Definition. If $(S, \leq)$ is an ordered set then the topology
generated by all sets of the form $]x, \infty[$ or $]-\infty, x[$, where
$x \in S$, is called the order topology of S. Relative to the order
topology, S is called an ordered space.

Examples.

(42) An order on a set S is called discrete if, for each
$x \in S$, there exists a, b $\in$ S such that $\{x\} =]a, b[$. A discrete
order induces the discrete topology, e. g., the natural order on
N.

(43) The order topology on R is the Euclidean topology.

(44) The order topology on Q is the relative Euclidean
topology.

(45) There exists a subset S of R such that the order
topology on S and the relative Euclidean topology on S are distinct.

Proposition 1.6. If S is an ordered set then the family of all sets of the form]a, b[(where a = -∞ and b = ∞ are allowed) is a base for the order topology.

Example.

(46) Let S be a well-ordered set which contains an element with uncountably many predecessors (i. e., there exists x ∈ S such that {y ∈ S : y < x} is uncountable). Let Ω denote the first such element and let ω denote the first element of S with infinitely many predecessors. (The existence of such a set S, as well as the elements Ω and ω, is a consequence of the well-ordering principle.) It can be proved that, given any two well-ordered sets, one is the image of an initial segment of the other under an order-preserving bijection. Consequently, no matter what set S one begins with, the sets

(*)   {0, 1, 2, ..., ω, ω + 1, ..., Ω}

are essentially identical, where 0 is the first element of S, 1 is the first element of S - {0}, ω + 1 is the first element greater than ω, etc. Hereafter we identify the sets (*), calling their members ordinal numbers. The space {0, 1, ..., ω} with the order topology is denoted $\mathcal{O}(ω)$ and the space {0, 1, ..., Ω} with the order topology is denoted $\mathcal{O}(Ω)$.

Show that no sequence in $\mathcal{O}(Ω)$ - {Ω} converges to Ω and hence the topology of $\mathcal{O}(Ω)$ cannot be described in terms of sequences. In particular, $\mathcal{O}(Ω)$ is not metrizable.

Definition. If X is a space, A ⊂ X, and p ∈ X, then p is called a limit point of A provided (N - {p}) ∩ A ≠ □ for each neighborhood N of p. The set of limit points of A is denoted Lp(A).

Examples.

(47) Lp(A) = □ for every subset A of a discrete space.

(48) If X is an indiscrete space and A is a nondegenerate

subset of X then Lp(A) = X.

(49) If X is a cofinite space and A is an infinite subset
of X then Lp(A) = X.

(50) In the space $\underset{\sim}{R}$, Lp([0, 1]) = Lp([0, 1] ∪ {2}).

Theorem 13. If (X, $\mathcal{J}$) is a space and A ⊂ B ⊂ X, then
Lp(A) ⊂ Lp(B). If M and N are subsets of X, then Lp(M ∪ N) =
Lp(M) ∪ Lp(N). Moreover, $\overline{A}$ = A ∪ Lp(A). Finally, if A ⊂ Y ⊂ X,
Y ≠ □ and if Lp(A, Y) denotes the set of limit points of A rel-
ative to $\mathcal{J}$(Y), then Lp(A, Y) = Lp(A) ∩ Y.

FOOTNOTE

[1]A set is nondegenerate if it contains more than one element.

2
CONNECTED SETS

The notion of a connected set is fundamental in topology. In an intuitive, natural sense the set R and the set $[0, 1]$ are connected, or "all of a piece," while the set $[0, 1] \cup [2, 3]$ is not connected, since it consists of two "discontinuous" pieces. The set Z fails to be connected in a very strong sense, since it is of many pieces. The intrinsic quality of R and $[0, 1]$, which is at the root of their connectedness, is subtler than simply not being the union of two disjoint sets. (After all, any non-degenerate set can be written as the union of disjoint, nonempty sets.) For a set to be disconnected, it must be the union of two nonempty sets which are separated in a sense made precise in the following definition.

Definition. Two subsets A and B of a space are separated if $\overline{A} \cap B = A \cap \overline{B} = \Box$.

We write $A|B$ if A and B are separated sets.

Proposition 2.1. If A, B, and C are subsets of a space then

   (i) $\Box|A$,
  (ii)   if $A|B$ then $B|A$,
 (iii)   if $A|B$ and $C \subset A$ then $C|B$,
  (iv)   if $A|B$ and $A|C$ then $A|(B \cup C)$,
   (v)   if $A|B$ then $A \cap C$ and $B \cap C$ are separated sets in the space C.

23

Examples.

(1) In a discrete space two sets are separated if and only if they are disjoint.

(2) In an indiscrete space two sets are separated if and only if one of them is empty.

(3) In a cofinite space two nonempty sets are separated if and only if they are disjoint and finite.

(4) In the set $\underset{\sim}{R}$ of real numbers let $\mathcal{R}$ denote the family of all sets $]-\infty$, $b[$ and all sets $[a, \infty[$, and let $\mathcal{J}_r = \mathcal{J}(\mathcal{R})$. Relative to $\mathcal{J}_r$ the intervals $[a, b[$ are open, and for this reason $\mathcal{J}_r$ is sometimes called the right half-open topology. The left half-open topology $\mathcal{J}_\ell$ is defined dually: if $\mathcal{L}$ is the family of all sets $]-\infty$, $b]$ and $]a, \infty[$, then $\mathcal{J}_\ell = \mathcal{J}(\mathcal{L})$.

A subset A of $(\underset{\sim}{R}, \mathcal{J}_r)$ is open if and only if A is the union of right half-open intervals, and the Euclidean topology is a subfamily of $\mathcal{J}_r$. For each real number t, the sets $]-\infty$, $t[$ and $[t, \infty[$ are separated, but the sets $]-\infty$, $t]$ and $]t, \infty[$ are not separated. Dual results hold for $(\underset{\sim}{R}, \mathcal{J}_\ell)$.

Theorem 14. If A and B are subsets of a space then the following statements are equivalent:

(i) $A|B$,

(ii) A and B are disjoint closed subsets with respect to the relative topology on $A \cup B$,

(iii) A and B are disjoint open subsets with respect to the relative topology on $A \cup B$.

Definition. A subset K of a space is connected if K is not the union of two nonempty separated sets.

Examples.

(5) A subset of a discrete space is connected if and only if it contains at most one element.

(6) Every subset of an indiscrete space is connected.

(7) All subsets of cofinite spaces are connected except for the finite, nondegenerate subsets.

Proposition 2.2. A subset K of $\underset{\sim}{R}$ is connected if and only if, for each a, b $\in$ K with a < b it follows that $[a, b] \subset K$.

In particular, $\underset{\sim}{R}$ is connected but $\underset{\sim}{Q}$ and $\underset{\sim}{R} - \underset{\sim}{Q}$ are not connected.

Example.

(8) In the space $(\underset{\sim}{R}, \mathcal{J}_r)$ a set is connected if and only if it contains at most one element.

Proposition 2.3. If X is a space and $K \subset Y \subset X$, then K is connected if and only if K is connected with respect to the relative topology on Y.

Example.

(9) If $\mathcal{J}_1$ and $\mathcal{J}_2$ are topologies on a set X with $\mathcal{J}_1 \subset \mathcal{J}_2$, and if K is a subset of X which is connected relative to $\mathcal{J}_2$, then K is connected relative to $\mathcal{J}_1$.

Definition. An ordered set S has the Dedekind property provided that for each decomposition S = A $\cup$ B, where A and B are nonempty and a < b whenever a $\in$ A and b $\in$ B, either A contains a maximal element or B contains a minimal element, but not both.

Theorem 15. A nondegenerate connected subset of an ordered space is infinite. An ordered space is connected if and only if it has the Dedekind property.

Examples.

(1)) In the space $\mathcal{O}(\Omega)$ a set is connected if and only if it contains at most one element.

(11) If A and B are ordered sets we define a relation $\leq$ on A $\times$ B as follows: $(a_1, b_1) \leq (a_2, b_2)$ if and only if $b_1 < b_2$,

or $b_1 = b_2$ and $a_1 \leq a_2$. Then $\leq$ is an order relation on $A \times B$ called the <u>lexicographic order</u>. Relative to the order topology $A \times B$ is a <u>lexicographic space</u>. The lexicographic space $[0, 1] \times [0, 1]$ is connected but the lexicographic space $\underset{\sim}{R} \times \underset{\sim}{R}$ is not connected.

Theorem <u>16</u>. If X is a space then the following statements are equivalent:

(i) X is connected,

(ii) X is not the union of two disjoint nonempty closed sets,

(iii) X is not the union of two disjoint nonempty open sets,

(iv) if $A \subset X$ and A is both open and closed then $A = \square$ or $A = X$,

(v) if $A \subset X$ and $\partial A = \square$ then $A = \square$ or $A = X$.

Theorem <u>17</u>. Let K, A, and B be subsets of a space such that $A|B$ and $K \subset A \cup B$. If K is connected then $K \subset A$ or $K \subset B$.

Theorem <u>18</u>. Let $\mathcal{Q}$ be a family of connected subsets of a space and let K be a connected subset which is separated from no member of $\mathcal{Q}$. Then $K \cup (\cup \mathcal{Q})$ is connected.

Corollary <u>12.1</u>. $\underset{\sim}{R}^n$ is connected.

(Hint: For the case n = 2 let K be the y axis and let $\mathcal{Q}$ be the family of all horizontal lines.)

Theorem <u>19</u>. If K is a connected set and $K \subset A \subset \overline{K}$, then A is a connected set.

Example.

(12) In $\underset{\sim}{R}^2$ let A_1 be the straight-line segment joining $(1, 0)$ and $(1/2, 1)$, let A_2 be the straight-line segment joining $(1/2, 1)$ and $(1/3, 0)$, and in general let A_{2n} be the straight-line segment joining $(1/2n, 1)$ and $(1/(2n + 1), 0)$, and let A_{2n+1} be the straight-line segment joining $(1/(2n + 1), 0)$ and

$(1/(2n + 2), 1)$. Let B be any subset of $\{(0, y) : 0 \leq y \leq 1\}$. Then $B \cup (\cup_{n=1}^{\infty} \{A_n\})$ is a connected subset of $\underset{\sim}{R}^2$. (See Figure 1.)

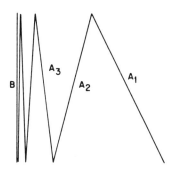

FIGURE 1

Definition. A subset C of a space X is a component of X provided C is connected and, if K is a connected set containing C, then K = C.

That is, the components of a space are the maximal connected subsets.

Example.

(13) The components of a discrete space are the singleton sets. However, a connected space is its only component. The components of $(\underset{\sim}{R}, \mathcal{J}_r)$, $(\underset{\sim}{R}, \mathcal{J}_\ell)$, $\mathcal{O}(\Omega)$, and $\underset{\sim}{Q}$ (with the relative Euclidean topology) are the singleton sets.

Proposition 2.4. If X is a space then each element of X lies in a unique component of X. Each component of X is a closed set. Two distinct components of X are separated.

Proposition 2.5. If C is a component of the space X and $C \subset Y \subset X$, then C is a component of the subspace Y.

Example.

(14) Let $\mathcal{J}_1$ and $\mathcal{J}_2$ be topologies on a set X with $\mathcal{J}_1 \subset \mathcal{J}_2$. Each component of X relative to $\mathcal{J}_2$ is a subset of some component relative to $\mathcal{J}_1$.

Definition. If S is a set and a, b $\in$ S, then a simple chain from a to b is a finite family $\mathcal{C} = \{C_1, C_2, \ldots, C_n\}$ of subsets of S such that a $\in C_1$, b $\in C_n$, and $C_i \cap C_j \neq \square$ if and only if $|i - j| \leq 1$.

Theorem 20. Let $\mathcal{J}$ be a family of connected open subsets of the space X such that X $= \bigcup \mathcal{J}$. Then X is connected if and only if, for each a, b $\in$ X, there exists a simple chain of members of $\mathcal{J}$ from a to b.

3
COMPACT SETS

The concept of compactness is among the most important
ideas of analysis, and it was studied extensively in Euclidean
spaces well before the notion of a topological space was con-
ceived. The compact subsets of a Euclidean space are simply the
closed sets with finite diameter. The idea of having finite
diameter does not translate readily into the terminology of
topological spaces, and even in metric spaces the closed sets
with finite diameter do not necessarily possess the essential
qualities of compact sets in Euclidean spaces. It is not immed-
iately apparent that the definition which follows is the appropriate one for arbitrary topological spaces, but the subsequent
results will justify it.

Definition. A cover of a set S is a family of sets whose
union contains S. If $S \subset X$ where X is a topological space, then
an open cover of S is a cover of S whose members are open subsets
of X.

Definition. A subset K of a space is compact if, for each
open cover $\mathcal{U}$ of K, there exist members U_1, U_2, ..., U_n of $\mathcal{U}$ such
that $\{U_1, U_2, ..., U_n\}$ is a cover of K. That is, K is compact
provided each open cover of K admits a finite subcover of K.

Examples.
(1) The compact subsets of a discrete space are the finite
subsets.
(2) In an indiscrete or cofinite space every subset is
compact.

29

Proposition 3.1. Any finite subset of any space is compact.
If X is á space and $K \subset Y \subset X$, then K is compact if and only if
K is compact with respect to the relative topology on Y.

Theorem 21. Let X be a space and let $\mathcal{B}$ be a base for its
topology. A subset K of X is compact if and only if each cover
of K by members of $\mathcal{B}$ admits a finite subcover of K.

Corollary 21.1. If a, b $\in \underset{\sim}{R}$ with a $\leq$ b then $[a, b]$ is
compact.

Theorem 22. A closed subset of a compact space is compact.
The union of a finite family of compact subsets of a space is
compact.

Corollary 22.1. The compact subsets of $\underset{\sim}{R}$ are precisely the
closed sets of finite diameter.

Examples.
(3) If $\mathcal{J}_1$ and $\mathcal{J}_2$ are topologies on a set X with $\mathcal{J}_1 \subset \mathcal{J}_2$
and if K is a subset of X which is compact with respect to $\mathcal{J}_2$,
then K is compact with respect to $\mathcal{J}_1$.
(4) A closed and "bounded" subset of an ordered space need
not be compact. Consider the ordered space $\underset{\sim}{Q}$ and its closed
subset $[0, 1] \cap \underset{\sim}{Q}$.

Theorem 23. An ordered space is compact if and only if each
nonempty subset has a least upper bound and a greatest lower
bound.

Example.
(5) A well-ordered space is compact if and only if it
contains a maximal element. In particular, $\mathcal{O}(\omega)$ and $\mathcal{O}(\Omega)$ are
compact spaces.

Definition. A family of sets has the finite intersection property (f. i. p.) provided each of its finite subfamilies has nonempty intersection.

Theorem 24. A space is compact if and only if each family of closed sets having the f. i. p. has nonempty intersection.

Theorem 25. A subset of R^n is compact if and only if it is closed and has finite diameter.

4

SEPARATION AXIOMS

Many theorems which are true, say for metric or Euclidean spaces, are not true for general topological spaces. For example, in Euclidean spaces every compact set is closed, but this result is not true for arbitrary spaces. (Consider an indiscrete space.) In an effort to state such theorems in the most general setting possible, an extensive hierarchy of special kinds of topological spaces has been developed. Because the definitions of such spaces are usually couched in terms of separating or distinguishing between various kinds of subsets, they are called separation axioms. We study here some of the more important separation axioms.

Definition. A space X is said to be a T_0 space if, for each x, y $\in$ X with x $\neq$ y, there exists an open set U such that either x $\in$ U and y $\in$ X - U or y $\in$ U and x $\in$ X - U. Moreover, X is a T_1 space if, for each x, y $\in$ X with x $\neq$ y, there exists an open set U such that x $\in$ U and y $\in$ X - U. Finally, X is a T_2 space if, for each x, y $\in$ X with x $\neq$ y, there exists an open set U such that x $\in$ U and y $\in$ X - $\overline{U}$. A T_2 space is also called a Hausdorff space.

Proposition 4.1. Every metric space is a Hausdorff space. If i = 0 or 1 then a T_{i+1} space is a T_i space. If i = 0, 1, or 2 then a subspace of a T_i space is a T_i space.

Examples.
(1) Discrete spaces are Hausdorff.

32

(2) A nondegenerate indiscrete space is not a T_0 space.

(3) An infinite cofinite space is a T_1 space which is not a T_2 space.

(4) Let $S = \{0, 1\}$ with topology $\mathcal{J} = \{\square, \{0\}, S\}$. Then $(S, \mathcal{J})$ is a T_0 space which is not a T_1 space. The space $(S, \mathcal{J})$ is called the Sierpinski space.

(5) If A is a subset of a T_1 space then $Lp(A)$ is a closed set.

(6) Ordered spaces and the spaces $(\underset{\sim}{R}, \mathcal{J}_r)$ and $(\underset{\sim}{R}, \mathcal{J}_\ell)$ are Hausdorff spaces. Thus $\mathcal{O}(\Omega)$ is a nonmetrizable Hausdorff space.

(7) In a Hausdorff space a sequence can converge to at most one point.

Theorem 26. Consider the following statements about a space X.

(i) if $x \neq y$ in X then $\overline{\{x\}} \neq \overline{\{y\}}$.

(ii) If $F \subset X$ and F is finite then F is closed.

(iii) If $x \in X$ then $\{x\} = \cap \{N : N$ is a neighborhood of $x\}$.

(iv) If $x \in X$ then $\{x\} = \cap \{N : N$ is a closed neighborhood of $x\}$.

(v) If $x \neq y$ in X then there exist disjoint neighborhoods of x and y.

Statement (i) holds if and only if X is a T_0 space. Further, statements (ii) and (iii) are each equivalent to the assertion that X is a T_1 space. Finally, (iv) and (v) are each equivalent to the assertion that X is a T_2 space.

Theorem 27. A compact subset of a Hausdorff space is closed. If X is a space in which compact subsets are closed, then X is a T_1 space.

Examples.

(8) There exists a T_1 space in which certain compact subsets are not closed.

(9)   There exists a non-Hausdorff space in which each compact subset is closed.   Let A be an infinite set and let X = A $\cup$ {p, q}, where p and q are distinct nonmembers of A.   Let $\mathcal{P}$ = {B $\cup$ {p} : B $\subset$ A and A - B is finite}, let $\mathcal{Q}$ = {B $\cup$ {q} : B $\subset$ A and A - B is finite}, and let $\mathcal{A}$ = {{a} : a $\in$ A}.   If $\mathcal{T}$ = $\mathcal{T}(\mathcal{P} \cup \mathcal{Q} \cup \mathcal{A})$ then (X, $\mathcal{T}$) is the desired space.

Definition.   A space X is _regular_ if, for each closed subset F of X and each x $\in$ X - F, there exists an open set U such that x $\in$ U $\subset$ $\bar{U}$ $\subset$ X - F.   The space X is _normal_ if, for each pair of disjoint closed sets F and K, there exists an open set U such that F $\subset$ U $\subset$ $\bar{U}$ $\subset$ X - K.   A T_3 _space_ is a regular T_1 space.   A T_4 _space_ is a normal T_1 space.

Examples.

(10)   A discrete space is a T_4 space.

(11)   A nondegenerate indiscrete space is both regular and normal but is neither T_3 nor T_4.

(12)   An infinite cofinite space is neither regular nor normal.

Proposition 4.2.   If i = 0, 1, 2, or 3, then a T_{i+1} space is a T_i space.   A subspace of a regular space is regular.   A closed subspace of a normal space is normal.

Theorem 28.   Consider the following statements about a space X.

(i)   If F is a closed subset of X and x $\in$ X - F, then there exist disjoint open sets U and V such that x $\in$ U and F $\subset$ V.

(ii)   If x $\in$ X and N is a neighborhood of x then N contains a closed neighborhood of x.

(iii)   If F and K are disjoint closed subsets of X, then there exist disjoint open sets U and V such that F $\subset$ U and K $\subset$ V.

(iv) If F is a closed subset of X and U is an open set
containing F, then there exists an open set V such that $F \subset V \subset$
$\overline{V} \subset U$.

Then (i) and (ii) are each equivalent to the assertion that
X is a regular space, and (iii) and (iv) are each equivalent to
the assertion that X is a normal space.

Theorem 29. A metric space is a T_4 space.

Theorem 30. An ordered space is a T_4 space.
(Hint: Let A and B be disjoint closed subsets of the ordered
space S. Consider first the case where no member of B lies between any two members of A, and show that there is an open inter-
val U such that $A \subset U \subset \overline{U} \subset S - B$. Otherwise, show that A =
$\cup \{A_\alpha\}$ where each A_α is closed and satisfies the first case.)

Examples.
(13) There exists a T_4 space which is not metrizable.
(14) There exists a Hausdorff space which is not regular.
Let $\underset{\sim}{R}$ have the topology generated by the Euclidean topology and
the family of sets $(]a,,b[- \underset{\sim}{Q}) \cup \{x\}$ where $a < x < b$.

Proposition 4.3. The space $(\underset{\sim}{R}, \mathcal{J}_r)$ is a T_4 space.

Theorem 31. A compact Hausdorff space is regular. A compact regular space is normal.

5
MAPPINGS

To a large extent, topology is concerned with properties of sets which are preserved by continuous functions. The notion of continuity of functions can be extended in a straightforward way from real-valued functions of a real variable--familiar to every calculus student--to functions defined on topological spaces. In fact, as is often the case with this sort of generalization, the abstracted definition is simpler than the classical "$\epsilon - \delta$" definition.

<u>Definition</u>. Let X and Y be spaces, $x_0 \in X$, and $f : X \to Y$ a function. The function f is <u>continuous</u> <u>at</u> x_0 if for each neighborhood N of $f(x_0)$ there exists a neighborhood M of x_0 such that $f(M) \subset N$. A function is <u>continuous</u> if it is continuous at each element of its domain. A continuous function is also called a <u>mapping</u>.

<u>Examples</u>.
(1) A function with discrete domain is continuous.
(2) A function with indiscrete range is continuous.
(3) Constant functions are continuous.

<u>Proposition 5.1</u>. Let X, Y, and Z be spaces and suppose $f : X \to Y$ and $g : Y \to Z$ are mappings. Then $gf : X \to Z$ is a mapping. If $A \subset X$ then $f|A$ is a mapping.

<u>Theorem 32</u>. If X and Y are spaces and $f : X \to Y$ is a function, then the following statements are equivalent.
(i) The function f is a mapping.

36

(ii)   If B is an open subset of Y then $f^{-1}(B)$ is an open subset of X.

(iii) If B is a closed subset of Y then $f^{-1}(B)$ is a closed subset of X.

(iv)   If $A \subset X$ then $f(\overline{A}) \subset \overline{f(A)}$.

(v)   If $B \subset Y$ then $\overline{f^{-1}(B)} \subset f^{-1}(\overline{B})$

(vi)   If $B \subset Y$ then $f^{-1}(B^{\circ}) \subset f^{-1}(B)^{\circ}$.

Example.

(4)   If $\mathcal{J}_1$ and $\mathcal{J}_2$ are topologies on a set X then the identity function $(X, \mathcal{J}_1) \rightarrow (X, \mathcal{J}_2)$ is continuous if and only if $\mathcal{J}_2 \subset \mathcal{J}_1$.

Proposition 5.2. Let X and Y be spaces and suppose the topology of Y is generated by a family $\mathcal{A}$. A function $f : X \rightarrow Y$ is continuous if and only if $f^{-1}(S)$ is open for each $S \in \mathcal{A}$.

Proposition 5.3. Suppose (X, ρ) and (Y, d) are metric spaces, $f : X \rightarrow Y$ is a function, and $a \in X$. The following statements are equivalent.

(i)   The function f is continuous at a.

(ii)   If $\epsilon > 0$ then there exists $\delta > 0$ such that $d(f(x), f(a)) < \epsilon$ whenever $\rho(x, a) < \delta$.

(iii) If x is a sequence in X and $\lim x = a$, then $\lim fx = f(a)$.

Examples.

(5)   If f and g are mappings of $\underline{R}$ into $\underline{R}$, then the functions $f + g$ and $f \cdot g$ (defined by $(f + g)(t) = f(t) + g(t)$ and $(f \cdot g)(t) = f(t) \cdot g(t)$) are continuous. Consequently, every polynomial with real coefficients is continuous.

(6)   Find examples of injective mappings f such that (i) f^{-1} is a mapping, (ii) f^{-1} is not a mapping.

(7)   Let $\{0, 1\}$ have the discrete topology. If X is a space and $A \subset X$, then the characteristic function of A,

$\chi_A : X \rightarrow \{0, 1\}$, is defined by

$$\chi_A(x) = \begin{cases} 1 & \text{if } x \in A, \\ 0 & \text{if } x \in X - A. \end{cases}$$

Show that χ_A is continuous at x if and only if $x \in X - \partial A$.

Theorem 33. If f is a mapping and K is a connected subset of the domain of f, then f(K) is connected.

Proposition 5.4. A space X is connected if and only if there exists no mapping from X onto the discrete space of two elements.

Proposition 5.5. If $f : X \rightarrow Y$ is a mapping and C is a component of Y, then $f^{-1}(C)$ is the union of some family of components of X.

Example.
(8) If $f : \underset{\sim}{R} \rightarrow \underset{\sim}{R}$ is continuous, $f(0) < 0$, and $f(1) > 0$, then there exists $t \in]0, 1[$ such that $f(t) = 0$.

Theorem 34. If f is a mapping and K is a compact subset of the domain of f, then f(K) is compact.

Corollary 34.1. If X is a compact space and $f : X \rightarrow \underset{\sim}{R}$ is continuous, then f(X) is closed and has finite diameter. In particular, there exist elements x_0 and x_1 of X such that $f(x_0) \leq f(x) \leq f(x_1)$ for all $x \in X$.

Example.
(9) None of the following properties is preserved by continuous surjections: open, closed, T_0, T_1, T_2, regular, normal, metrizable. However, if $f : X \rightarrow Y$ is continuous surjection which preserves closed sets and if X is normal, then Y is normal.

Proposition 5.6. Suppose X is a space, Y is a T_2 space, and f and g are mappings from X into Y. Then $\{x \in X : f(x) = g(x)\}$ is a closed set. If f is injective, then X is a T_2 space.

Definition. An injective mapping $f : X \to Y$ is a homeomorphism provided $f^{-1} : f(X) \to X$ is a mapping. If f is a bijective homeomorphism then X and Y are homeomorphic or topologically equivalent.

Examples.

(10) Discrete (respectively, indiscrete, cofinite) spaces are homeomorphic if and only if they have the same cardinality.

(11) For each $n \in N$, define

$$S^n = \{x \in \underline{R}^{n+1} : \sum_{i=1}^{n+1} x_i^2 = 1\}.$$

An n-sphere is a space homeomorphic to S^n. If $p \in S^n$ and $n > 0$, then $S^n - \{p\}$ is the continuous image of $\underline{R}^n$ and hence S^n is connected.

(12) If $n = 1, 2, \ldots$, then an n-cell is a set which is homeomorphic to $I^n = \{x \in \underline{R}^n : 0 \le x_i \le 1\}$. An n-cell is homeomorphic to $\{x \in \underline{R}^n : \sum_{i=1}^{n} x_i^2 \le 1\}$, the closed n-ball. The boundary of an n-cell if homeomorphic to S^{n-1}.

Proposition 5.7. Inverses of homeomorphisms are homeomorphisms. The composition of homeomorphisms is a homeomorphism. If h is a homeomorphism and A is a subset of the domain of h, then $h|A$ is a homeomorphism.

Proposition 5.8. If X and Y are spaces and $f : X \to Y$ is a bijection, then the following statements are equivalent.

(i) The bijection f is a homeomorphism.

(ii) If $A \subset X$ then $f(\overline{A}) = \overline{f(A)}$.

(iii) If $A \subset X$ then $f(A^o) = f(A)^o$.

Examples.

(13) Surjective homeomorphisms preserve the following properties: discrete, indiscrete, cofinite, open, closed, T_0, T_1, T_2, regular, normal, metrizable, ordered.

(14) The following sets are all homeomorphic to each other: $\mathbb{R}$, $]0, 1[$, $]0, \infty[$, $\{x \in \mathbb{R}^2 : x_2 = x_1^2\}$, $\{x \in \mathbb{R}^2 : x_2 = x_1 \sin (1/x_1)\} \cup \{(0, 0)\}$. Thus the property of being of finite diameter is <u>not</u> preserved by homeomorphisms.

(15) A bijective mapping need not be a homeomorphism.

Theorem <u>35</u>. If X is a compact space, Y is a T_2 space, and f : X → Y is a continuous injection, then f is a homeomorphism.

Definition. A metric space is <u>bounded</u> if it has finite diameter.

Theorem <u>36</u>. Every metric space is homeomorphic to a bounded metric space.

6
PRODUCT SPACES

We have already considered a topology on the Cartesian product of spaces in a very special case, that of $\underset{\sim}{R}^n$. In this section we consider the more general problem of attaching a topology to the product of arbitrary topological spaces. There is no difficulty in seeing that this can be done in a number of ways, and in certain situations one may wish to impose different topologies on Cartesian products. For most topological purposes, however, the definition which follows is the most useful.

First, we shall widen the class of Cartesian products to embrace arbitrary families, rather than just finite families.

We defined $X_1 \times X_2$ to be the set of ordered pairs (x_1, x_2) with $x_1 \in X_1$ and $x_2 \in X_2$. We then identified $X_1 \times X_2 \times \cdots \times X_n$ with the set of ordered n-tuples $(x_1, x_2, \ldots, x_n)$, where $x_i \in X_i$ for each $i = 1, 2, \ldots, n$. Presumably, a member of the product of an infinite family of sets is to be a very large "ordered tuple" with a distinct coordinate value chosen from each set of the family. Such an object, then, would associate with each member of the family an element of that member. This description coincides precisely with the notion of a choice function for the family of sets. Thus (returning for a moment to the case of a finite family) the element (x_1, x_2) of $X_1 \times X_2$ can be identified with the function $x : \{X_1, X_2\} \to X_1 \cup X_2$ which is defined by $x(X_i) = x_i$ for $i = 1, 2$. If $\mathcal{X}$ is a denumerable family of sets, $\mathcal{X} = \{X_1, X_2, \ldots\}$, then a member of the Cartesian product of $\mathcal{X}$ is a sequence whose n-th term is always a member of X_n. The general definition follows.

Definition. If $\mathcal{X}$ is a nonempty family of sets then the Cartesian product of $\mathcal{X}$ (more briefly, the product of $\mathcal{X}$) is the set of all functions $y : \mathcal{X} \to \cup \mathcal{X}$ such that $y(X) \in X$ for each $X \in \mathcal{X}$.

The product of $\mathcal{X}$ is denoted $\Pi \mathcal{X}$.

With each $X \in \mathcal{X}$ there is associated a function $\pi_X : \Pi \mathcal{X} \to X$ defined by

$$\pi_X(y) = y(X).$$

The function π_X is called a projection function. Occasionally it is convenient to write $\mathcal{X} = \{X_\alpha : \alpha \in A\}$ and define $x_\alpha = \pi_\alpha(x)$.

Remark. In the case $\mathcal{X} = \{X_1, X_2, \ldots, X_n\}$ we identify $\Pi \mathcal{X}$ with $X_1 \times X_2 \times \cdots \times X_n$, and in this case the i-th projection function $\pi_i = \pi_{X_i}$ is defined by

$$\pi_i(x) = \pi_i(x_1, x_2, \ldots, x_n) = x_i,$$

for each $i = 1, 2, \ldots, n$.

Definition. If $\mathcal{X}$ is a nonempty family of topological spaces, let

$$\mathcal{A} = \{\pi_X^{-1}(U) : X \in \mathcal{X} \text{ and } U \text{ is an open subset of } X\}.$$

The topology $\mathcal{T}(\mathcal{A})$ is called the product topology on $\Pi \mathcal{X}$.

Whenever $\Pi \mathcal{X}$ is to be regarded as a topological space, and unless the contrary is stated specifically, the product topology is always assumed.

Proposition 6.1. If $\mathcal{X} = \{X_\alpha : \alpha \in A\}$ is a nonempty family of spaces, then the sets of the form

$$\bigcap_{i=1}^{n} \{\pi_{\alpha_i}^{-1}(U_i)\}$$

form a base for the product topology on $\Pi \mathcal{X}$, where each U_i is an open subset of X_{α_i}. Moreover, the projection functions are continuous.

Examples.

(1) The product of a finite family of discrete spaces is a discrete space.

(2) The product of an infinite family of nondegenerate discrete spaces is _not_ a discrete space.

(3) The product of a family of indiscrete spaces is an indiscrete space.

Proposition 6.2. The product and Euclidean topologies on $\underset{\sim}{R}^n$ are identical. More generally, if M_1, M_2, ..., M_n are metric spaces then $M_1 \times M_2 \times \cdots \times M_n$ is metrizable.

Proposition 6.3. If X is a space, Y is a Hausdorff space, and f : X → Y is continuous, then $\{(x, f(x)) : x \in X\}$ is a closed subset of X × Y. Consequently, a space X is a Hausdorff space if and only if the diagonal[1] of X × X is a closed set.

Proposition 6.4. Suppose $\mathcal{X} = \{X_\alpha : \alpha \in A\}$ is a family of spaces and $A_\alpha \subset X_\alpha$ for each $\alpha \in A$. If $\mathcal{A} = \{A_\alpha : \alpha \in A\}$ then the product topology on $\Pi\mathcal{A}$ is identical with the relative topology on $\Pi\mathcal{A}$, regarded as a subspace of $\Pi\mathcal{X}$.

Examples.

(4) The product of a finite family of compact spaces is a compact space.

(5) If (M, ρ) is a metric space then $\rho : M \times M \to \underset{\sim}{R}$ is continuous.

(6) If (M, ρ) is a metric space and $\square \neq A \subset M$, we define $\rho(x, A) = g. 1. b.\{\rho(x, a) : a \in A\}$ for each $x \in M$. Then $\rho(x, A) : M \to \underset{\sim}{R}$ is continuous.

Theorem 37. The product of a family of T_0 (respectively, T_1, T_2, regular) spaces is a T_0 (respectively, T_1, T_2, regular) space.

Examples.

(7) If $S = \mathcal{O}(\Omega) \times \mathcal{O}(\omega) - \{(\Omega, \omega)\}$ then S is a nonnormal subspace of a normal space. To see this, consider the closed subsets $S \cap (\{\Omega\} \times \mathcal{O}(\omega))$ and $S \cap (\mathcal{O}(\Omega) \times \{\omega\})$. Note also that S is an example of a nonnormal T_3 space

(8) This is an example of two normal spaces whose product is not a normal space. In $(\mathcal{O}(\Omega) - \{\Omega\}) \times \mathcal{O}(\Omega)$ consider the closed subsets $(\mathcal{O}(\Omega) - \{\Omega\}) \times \{\Omega\}$ and $\{(x, x) : x \in \mathcal{O}(\Omega) - \{\Omega\}\}$.

Example 8 can be improved upon. Specifically, we can exhibit a normal space X such that $X \times X$ is not normal. To facilitate the discussion it is helpful to introduce the notion of a separable space.

Definition. A subset D of a space X is dense if $\overline{D} = X$. A space is separable if it contains a countable dense subset.

Examples.

(9) A discrete space is separable if and only if it is countable.

(10) Any indiscrete or cofinite space is separable.

(11) The space $\mathcal{O}(\Omega)$ is not separable.

Proposition 6.5. Euclidean spaces are separable. The space $(\underset{\sim}{R}, \mathcal{J}_r)$ is separable.

Example.

(12) The space $(\underset{\sim}{R}, \mathcal{J}_r)$ is a normal space but $(\underset{\sim}{R}, \mathcal{J}_r) \times (\underset{\sim}{R}, \mathcal{J}_r)$ is not a normal space.

(Hint: Observe that $\{(x, -x) : x \in \underset{\sim}{R}\}$ is a closed, discrete subspace of $(\underset{\sim}{R}, \mathcal{J}_r) \times (\underset{\sim}{R}, \mathcal{J}_r)$. Hence, to complete the argument it is sufficient to prove the next proposition.)

Proposition 6.6. A separable normal space cannot contain a closed, discrete subspace of cardinality c.

(Hint: If D is countable and $\overline{D}$ = X, choose a closed discrete subspace S of X; thus every subset of S is a closed subset of X. Using the normality of X, there exists an injective function from the family of subsets of S into the family of subsets of D.)

Definition. If X and Y are spaces, then a surjection f : X → Y is open provided f(U) is open for each open subset U of X.

Example.

(13) The composition of open surjections is open. However, if f : X → Y is an open surjection and A ⊂ X then it does not follow that f|A : A → f(A) is open.

Proposition 6.7. The projection mappings on a product space are open.

Theorem 38. Let Y be a space and let $\mathcal{X}$ = {X_α : $\alpha \in A$} be a family of spaces. For each $X_\alpha \in \mathcal{X}$, suppose f_α : Y → X is a mapping. The function f : Y → $\Pi\mathcal{X}$ defined by

$$\pi_\alpha f(y) = f_\alpha(y)$$

is a mapping.

Corollary 38.1. If A is a nonempty set and if {X_α : $\alpha \in A$} and {Y_α : $\alpha \in A$} are families of spaces such that X_α and Y_α are homeomorphic for each $\alpha \in A$, then Π{X_α : $\alpha \in A$} and Π{Y_α : $\alpha \in A$} are homeomorphic.

Theorem 39. Let $\mathcal{X}$ = {X_α : $\alpha \in A$} be a family of spaces, and for each $X_\alpha \in \mathcal{X}$ suppose $A_\alpha \subset X_\alpha$. Then

$$\overline{\Pi\{A_\alpha : \alpha \in A\}} = \Pi\{\overline{A}_\alpha : \alpha \in A\}.$$

If $\mathcal{X}$ = {X_1, ..., X_n} then

$$(\prod_{i=1}^{n} \{A_i\})^o = \prod_{i=1}^{n} \{A_i^o\},$$

and

$$\partial \prod_{i=1}^{n} \{A_i\} = \bigcup_{j=1}^{n} \{ \prod_{i=1}^{n} \{B_{ji}\}\}$$

where $B_{ji} = \overline{A}_i$ if $i \neq j$ and $B_{ii} = \partial A_i$.

Theorem 40. The product of a countable family of metric spaces is metrizable.

(Hint: If M_1, M_2, ... are metric spaces with metrics ρ_1, ρ_2, ..., and if each $\rho_n \leq 1$, let

$$\rho(x, y) = \sum_{n=1}^{\infty} 2^{-n} \rho_n(x_n, y_n)$$

for each $x, y \in \prod_{n=1}^{\infty} \{M_n\}$.)

Theorem 41. The product of a family of connected spaces is a connected space.

(Hint: If X_1, X_2, ..., X_n are members of the family $\mathcal{X}$ and if $p \in \Pi\mathcal{X}$, let

$$K(p, X_1, \ldots, X_n) = \{x \in \Pi\mathcal{X} : \pi_X(x) = \pi_X(p) \text{ if } X \neq X_i,$$
$$i = 1, \ldots, n\}$$

and show that $K(p, X_1, \ldots, X_n)$ is connected.)

FOOTNOTE

[1] If S is a set then the diagonal of $S \times S$ is $\{(x, x) : x \in S\}$.

7

COUNTABILITY AXIOMS

We begin by returning to the notion of a separable space.

Proposition 7.1. Separability is preserved by surjective mappings. Open subspaces of separable spaces are separable.

Example.

(1) A separable space may contain a closed, nonseparable subspace.

Theorem 42. If $\mathcal{A}$ is a family of separable spaces and $\#\mathcal{A} \leq c$, then $\Pi\mathcal{A}$ is separable.

(Hint: Assume $\mathcal{A} = \{X_\alpha : \alpha \in A\}$ with A a dense subset of $\underset{\sim}{R}$, and for each $\alpha \in A$ let $D_\alpha = \{x_1^\alpha, x_2^\alpha, \ldots\}$ be a countable dense subset of X_α. Let T be the set of all $(2n + 1)$-tuples $\tau = (r_1, r_2, \ldots, r_n, k_0, k_1, \ldots, k_n)$ where each $r_i \in Q$, $r_i < r_{i+1}$, and each $k_n \in \underset{\sim}{N}$. For each $\tau \in T$ let $x^\tau \in \Pi\mathcal{A}$ be defined by

$$
x^\tau(\alpha) = \begin{cases}
x_{k_0}^\alpha & \text{if } \alpha \leq r_1, \\
x_{k_i}^\alpha & \text{if } r_i < \alpha \leq r_{i+1} \\
x_{k_n}^\alpha & \text{if } r_n < \alpha.
\end{cases}
$$

Example.

(2) Any family of disjoint, nonempty open subsets of $\underset{\sim}{R}^n$ is countable.

Definition. A space X satisfies the first axiom of countability (more briefly, X is first countable) if, for each $x \in X$,

there exists a countable family $\mathcal{n}_x$ of neighborhoods of x such
that every neighborhood of x contains a member of $\mathcal{n}_x$. The space
X satisfies the <u>second</u> <u>axiom</u> <u>of</u> <u>countability</u> (or is <u>second</u>
<u>countable</u>) if the topology of X admits a countable base.

Examples.

(3) A discrete space is second countable if and only if
it is countable, but all discrete spaces are first countable.

(4) Indiscrete spaces are second countable.

(5) A cofinite space is first countable if and only if it
is countable.

Proposition 7.2. Every second countable space is both
separable and first countable. Every metric space is first
countable. The Euclidean space $\underset{\sim}{R}^n$ is second countable.

Examples.

(6) $(\underset{\sim}{R}, \mathcal{J}_r)$ is first countable and separable but not
second countable.

(7) The space $\mathcal{O}(\cap)$ is not first countable. The subspace
$\mathcal{O}(\cap) - \{\cap\}$ is first countable but not second countable.

Proposition 7.3. A subspace of a first (second) countable
space is first (second) countable. Continuous, open surjections
preserve both countability axioms.

Example.

(8) Theorem 11 is valid for first countable spaces as well
as for metric spaces.

Proposition 7.4. The product of a countable family of
first (second) countable spaces is first (second) countable.

Example.

(9) If $\mathcal{A}$ is an uncountable family of nondegenerate Hausdorff
spaces then $\Pi\mathcal{A}$ cannot be second countable.

Theorem 43. (Lindelof.) An open cover of a second countable space admits a countable subcover.

Definition. A Lindelof space is a space satisfying the conclusion of Theorem 43, i.e., a space such that each open cover admits a countable subcover.

Examples.

(10) A compact space is a Lindelof space and hence there exists a Lindelof space which is not separable and which satisfies neither of the countability axioms.

(11) A discrete space is Lindelof if and only if it is countable.

Theorem 44. Continuous surjections preserve the property of being a Lindelof space. A closed subspace of a Lindelof space is a Lindelof space.

Examples.

(12) There exists a Lindelof space such that certain subspaces are not Lindelof.

(13) $(\underset{\sim}{R}, \mathcal{J}_r)$ is a Lindelof space but $(\underset{\sim}{R}, \mathcal{J}_r) \times (\underset{\sim}{R}, \mathcal{J}_r)$ is not a Lindelof space.

Theorem 45. A Lindelof T_1 space is regular if and only if it is normal.

Theorem 45 will have great importance when we study the metrization problem. It also provides a quick and easy proof that $(\underset{\sim}{R}, \mathcal{J}_r)$ is a normal space (Proposition 4.3.).

Theorem 46. If M is a metric space then the following statements are equivalent.

(i) The space M is a separable space.

(ii) The space M is second countable.

(iii) The space M is a Lindelof space.

Example.

(14)   The space $(\underset{\sim}{R}, \mathcal{J}_r)$ is a separable, Lindelof T_4 space which is not metrizable.

Definition.   A subset K of a space X is <u>countably compact</u> if each countable open cover of K admits a finite subcover.

Examples.

(15)   In a discrete space the countably compact sets are precisely the compact sets.

(16)   Every compact set is countably compact but the converse is not true.   (Consider the set $\mathcal{O}(\cap) - \{\cap\}$.)

(17)   A Lindelof space is compact if and only if it is countably compact.

Theorem 47.   The property of being countably compact is preserved by continuous surjections.   A closed subset of a countably compact space is countably compact.

Theorem 48.   If each sequence in the space X has a cluster point, then X is countably compact.   Conversely, if X is a countably compact T_1 space, then each sequence in X has a cluster point.

Definition.   A space X is <u>sequentially compact</u> if each sequence in X has a convergent subsequence.

Theorem 49.   A sequentially compact space is countably compact.   Among first countable T_1 spaces the converse is true.

Proposition 7.5.   The property of being sequentially compact is preserved by continuous surjections.   A closed subspace of a sequentially compact space is sequentially compact.

Theorem 50.   If $\mathcal{X}$ is a countable family of countably compact, first countable T_1 spaces, then $\Pi\mathcal{X}$ is countably compact.

Theorem 51. A countably compact metric space is separable.

Corollary 51.1. If M is a metric space then the following statements are equivalent.

(i)   The space M is compact.

(ii) The space M is countably compact.

(iii) The space M is sequentially compact.

Consequently, the product of a countable family of compact metric spaces is a compact metric space.

8
COMPLETE SPACES AND PERFECT SETS

<u>Definition</u>. Let (X, ρ) be a metric space and suppose x is a sequence in X. if

$$\lim_{m,n \to \infty} \rho(x_m, x_n) = 0$$

then x is a <u>Cauchy sequence</u>. If every Cauchy sequence in X is convergent then (X, ρ) is <u>complete</u>.

<u>Examples</u>.

(1) In a metric space every convergent sequence is a Cauchy sequence. The converse fails.

(2) With respect to the Euclidean metric, the space $\underset{\sim}{R}$ is complete but $]0, 1[$ is not. Thus completeness is not a topological property.

<u>Definition</u>. A metrizable space is <u>topologically complete</u> if it is complete with respect to some metric which generates its topology.

<u>Example</u>.

(3) Discrete spaces are topologically complete.

<u>Theorem 52</u>. A closed subspace of a complete metric space is complete. A complete subspace of a metric space is a closed set. The product of a countable family of complete metric spaces is a topologically complete metrizable space.

<u>Theorem 53</u>. An open subspace of a complete metric space is topologically complete.

(Hint: If U is an open subset of the complete metric space
(M, ρ), let

$$d(x, y) = \frac{\left| \rho(x, M - U) - \rho(y, M - U) \right|}{1 + \left| \rho(x, M - U) - \rho(y, M - U) \right|}.)$$

Theorem 54. A compact metric space is complete.

Definition. A metric space (X, ρ) is totally bounded if,
for each $\epsilon > 0$, there exist $x_1, \ldots, x_{n(\epsilon)} \in X$ such that
$X \subset \cup_{i=1}^{n(\epsilon)} \{S(x_i, \epsilon)\}$.

Examples.
(4) A totally bounded metric space is bounded, but the
converse is not true.
(5) A subspace of a totally bounded metric space is totally
bounded.

Proposition 8.1. A compact metric space is totally bounded.
A totally bounded metric space is separable.

Theorem 55. A metric space is compact if and only if it is
complete and totally bounded.

Definition. A subset A of a space X is nowhere dense if
$(\overline{A})^o = \square$. If A is the union of a countable family of nowhere
dense sets then A is meager in X. A space X is meager if it is
meager in itself.

Examples.
(6) The set $\underset{\sim}{Z}$ is nowhere dense in $\underset{\sim}{R}$ and hence $\underset{\sim}{Z}$ is meager
in $\underset{\sim}{R}$. However, $\underset{\sim}{Z}$ is not meager. The set $\underset{\sim}{Q}$ is a dense, meager
subset of $\underset{\sim}{R}$. Moreover, $\underset{\sim}{Q}$ is meager.
(7) Discrete and indiscrete spaces are not meager.
(8) An infinite cofinite space is meager if and only if it
is countable.

Theorem 56.   If A is a subset of the space X then A is nowhere dense if and only if $A \subset \overline{X - \overline{A}}$. The union of a finite family of nowhere dense sets is a nowhere dense set.   If $A \subset Y \subset X$ and A is nowhere dense in the space Y, then A is nowhere dense in X.   The union of a countable family of sets which are meager in X is a set which is meager in X.   If $A \subset Y \subset X$ and A is meager in Y, then A is meager in X.

Theorem 57.   (Baire.)   No complete metric space is meager.

Definition.   A subset P of a space X is perfect if $P = Lp(P)$.

Example.

(9)   The only perfect subset of a discrete space is $\square$.   If X is an indiscrete space or an infinite cofinite space, then its perfect subsets are $\square$ and X.

Proposition 8.2.   Perfect sets are closed.   If $A \subset Lp(A)$ then $\overline{A}$ is perfect.

Theorem 58.   Every nonempty perfect subset of a complete metric space is uncountable.

Example.

(10)   Recall that if $x \in [0, 1]$ then x has a ternary representation: $x = \sum_{n=1}^{\infty} x_n 3^{-n}$, where $x_n = 0, 1,$ or 2.   The Cantor set $\mathcal{C}$ consists of all $x \in [0, 1]$ which have a ternary representation in which each $x_m \neq 1$.   If we define U_1^1 to be the open "middle third" of $[0, 1]$, i. e., $U_1^1 =]1/3, 2/3[$, and if $U_1^{n+1}, \ldots$ $U_{2^n}^{n+1}$ are the open "middle thirds" of $[0, 1] - \cup \{U_k^j : 1, \ldots, n;$ $k = 1, \ldots, 2^{j-1}\}$ (so that $U_1^2 =]1/9, 2/9[, U_2^2 =]7/9, 8/9[, U_1^3 =]1/27, 2/27[$, etc.), then

$$\mathcal{C} = [0, 1] - \cup \{U_j^n : n = 1, 2, \ldots ; j = 1, \ldots, 2^{n-1}\}.$$

Moreover, $\mathcal{C}$ is a compact, perfect subset of $[0, 1]$ and hence $\mathcal{C}$ is uncountable.

Definition. A subset A of a space is <u>scattered</u> provided, for each nonempty $B \subset A$, the set $B - Lp(B)$ is not empty.

That is, a set is scattered if each of its nonempty subsets has isolated points.

Example.

(11) Every discrete subspace of a space is scattered. There exists a nondiscrete scattered subset of $\underset{\sim}{R}$.

Theorem 59. If X is a perfect space then each scattered subset of X is nowhere dense. In a T_1 space the union of two scattered subsets is scattered.

Theorem 60. Every T_1 space is the union of a perfect set and a scattered set.

Theorem 61. A subset A of a T_1 space X is scattered if and only if for each perfect subset P of X it follows that $A \cap P$ is nowhere dense in P.

Definition. Let A be a subset of a space X. An element p of X is a <u>condensation point</u> of A, provided each neighborhood of p meets A in an uncountable set. The set of condensation points of A is denoted Con(A).

Proposition 8.3. If X is a space and $A \subset X$ then Con(A) is a closed set.

Theorem 62. If X is a second countable space and $A \subset X$ then $A - Con(A)$ is countable.

Theorem 63. If X is a space and A and B are subsets of X then

(i) $Con(A \cup B) = Con(A) \cup Con(B)$,
(ii) $Con(A) - Con(B) \subset Con(A - B)$,

(iii)   if $A \subset B$ then $Con(A) \subset Con(B)$,

(iv) $Con(A) \subset Lp(A) \subset \overline{A}$.

Moreover, if X is second countable, then

(v) $Con(A - Con(A)) = \square$,

(vi) $Con(Con(A)) = Con(A)$.

Theorem 64. Every scattered subset of a second countable space is countable.

Corollary 64.1. (Cantor-Bendixson.) A second countable space is the union of a perfect set and a countable set.

Notation. Let x and y be Cauchy sequences in the metric space (X, ρ). We write $x \sim y$ in the case $\lim_{n \to \infty} \rho(x_n, y_n) = 0$. It is readily verified that $\sim$ is an equivalence relation on the set of Cauchy sequences in X. The symbol $[x]$ denotes the equivalence class of which x is a member and $\widetilde{X}$ denotes the set of such equivalence classes.

Theorem 65. If (X, ρ) is a metric space, define $\widetilde{\rho}$ on $\widetilde{X} \times \widetilde{X}$ by

$$\widetilde{\rho}([x], [y]) = \lim_{n \to \infty} \rho(x_n, y_n).$$

Then $(\widetilde{X}, \widetilde{\rho})$ is a complete metric space.

Definition. The metric space $(\widetilde{X}, \widetilde{\rho})$ is called the completion of (X, ρ).

Definition. An isometry between metric spaces (X, ρ) and (Y, σ) is a function $f : X \to Y$ such that $\sigma(f(x_1), f(x_2)) = \rho(x_1, x_2)$ for all $(x_1, x_2) \in X \times X$. The spaces (X, ρ) and (Y, σ) are isometric if there exists a surjective isometry between them.

Example.

(12) An isometry is a homeomorphism.

Corollary 65.1. Every metric space is isometric to a dense subspace of some complete metric space.

Definition. Let (X, ρ) and (Y, σ) be metric spaces. A function $f : X \to Y$ is <u>uniformly</u> continuous if, for each $\epsilon > 0$, there exists $\delta > 0$ such that if $\rho(x_1, x_2) < \delta$ then $\sigma(f(x_1), f(x_2)) < \epsilon$.

Examples.

(13) A uniformly continuous function is continuous. If X has the discrete metric $(\rho(x_1, x_2) = 1$ if $x_1 \neq x_2)$ and Y is a metric space, then every function $f : X \to Y$ is uniformly continuous.

(14) The uniform continuity of $f : X \to Y$ with respect to one metric on X does not imply uniform continuity with respect to a topologically equivalent metric.

Proposition 8.4. The composition of uniformly continuous functions is uniformly continuous. If $f : (X, \rho) \to (Y, \sigma)$ is uniformly continuous, $A \subset X$, and $\rho_A = \rho | (A \times A)$, then $(f|A) : (A, \rho_A) \to (Y, \sigma)$ is uniformly continuous.

Theorem 66. If X is a compact metric space, Y is a metric space, and $f : X \to Y$ is continuous, then f is uniformly continuous.

Definition. Let A, B, and C be sets with $A \subset B$. If $f : A \to C$ and $g : B \to C$ are functions such that $f = g|A$, then g is an <u>extension</u> of f.

Proposition 8.5. If X is a space, Y is a Hausdorff space, $A \subset X$, and $f : A \to Y$ is a mapping, then f has at most one continuous extension $g : \overline{A} \to Y$.

Theorem 67. Let X be a metric space, Y a complete metric

space, and $A \subset X$. If $f : A \to Y$ is a uniformly continuous function then f admits a unique uniformly continuous extension
$\tilde{f} : \overline{A} \to Y$.

Theorem 68. The completion of a metric space is unique up
to isometry. That is, if X is a metric space isometric to
dense subsets of the complete metric spaces Y and Z, then Y and
Z are isometric.

9

INVERSE LIMITS

Definition. If X_0, X_1, X_2, ... is a sequence of spaces and if $f_n : X_{n+1} \to X_n$ is a sequence of mappings, then the sequence (X_n, f_n) is an inverse-limit sequence. The mappings f_n are bonding mappings. Define

$$\lim_{\leftarrow} X_n = \{x \in \prod_{n=0}^{\infty} \{X_n\} : x_n = f_n(x_{n+1}) \text{ for each } n \in \underset{\sim}{N}\}.$$

With the relative topology inherited from $\prod_{n=0}^{\infty} \{X_n\}$, the space $\lim_{\leftarrow} X_n$ is called the inverse limit of the inverse-limit sequence (X_n, f_n). An alternative notation is $X_\infty = \lim_{\leftarrow} X_n$.

Examples.

(1) Let X be any space, $X_n = X$, and $f_n(x) = x$ for each $n \in \underset{\sim}{N}$. Then X_∞ and X are homeomorphic.

(2) Let $X_n = [0, 2^{-n}]$ and $f_n(x) = x$ for each $n \in \underset{\sim}{N}$. Then X_∞ consists of a single point.

Proposition 9.1. If (X_n, f_n) is an inverse sequence of Hausdorff spaces then X_∞ is a closed subset of $\prod\{X_n\}$. If the bonding mappings are surjective then $X_\infty \neq \square$.

Theorem 69. The inverse limit of a sequence of compact metric spaces is nonempty and is a compact metric space.

Theorem 70. If (X_n, f_n) and (Y_n, g_n) are inverse-limit sequences and if there exists a sequence of mappings $h_n : X_n \to Y_n$ such that $g_n h_{n+1} = h_n f_n$, then the sequence h_n induces a mapping $h : X_\infty \to Y_\infty$ which is unique with respect to satisfying the condition $\pi_n h = h_n \pi_n$ for each $n \in \underset{\sim}{N}$. If each h_n is injective then

h is injective, and if each h_n is a homeomorphism then h is a
homeomorphism.

Theorem 71. Let (X_n, f_n) be an inverse-limit sequence, let
$X_{p(n)}$ be a subsequence of X_n, and let $g_n : X_{p(n+1)} \to X_{p(n)}$ be
the composition $g_n = f_{p(n)} f_{(p(n)+1)} \cdots f_{(p(n+1)-1)}$. Then
$(X_{p(n)}, g_n)$ is an inverse-limit sequence and $\varprojlim X_n$ and $\varprojlim X_{p(n)}$
are homeomorphic.

Definition. A space X is totally disconnected if its components are all singleton sets.

Examples.
(3) Discrete spaces, $(\underset{\sim}{R}, \mathcal{J}_r)$ and $\mathcal{O}(\Omega)$ are totally disconnected spaces.
(4) The spaces $\underset{\sim}{Q}$ and $\underset{\sim}{C}$ are totally disconnected spaces.

Proposition 9.2. A subspace of a totally disconnected
space is totally disconnected. The product of a family of totally disconnected spaces is totally disconnected.

Theorem 72. If $X_{\bullet}$ is a compact, totally disconnected Hausdorff space and if x and y are distinct elements of X, then there
exist disjoint closed subsets M and N of X such that $X = M \cup N$,
$x \in M$, and $y \in N$.

Theorem 73. The topology of a compact, totally disconnected
Hausdorff space has a base consisting of sets with empty boundary.

Theorem 74. If X is a compact, totally disconnected metric
space, then there exists a sequence $\mathcal{U}_n$ of open covers of X such
that
(i)   if $U, V \in \mathcal{U}_n$ then $U \cap V = \square$,
(ii) if $U \in \mathcal{U}_n$ then $\mathrm{diam}(U) < 2^{-n}$,
(iii) if $V \in \mathcal{U}_{n+1}$ then there exists $U \in \mathcal{U}_n$ such that $V \subset U$.

Theorem 75. Any compact, totally disconnected metric space
is homeomorphic to the inverse limit of a sequence of finite,
discrete spaces.

Theorem 76. Any two compact, totally disconnected, perfect
metric spaces are homeomorphic. In particular, $\underset{\sim}{C}$ is homeomorphic
to the space $2^{\underset{\sim}{N}}$, i. e., the product of a denumerable family of
discrete, two-point spaces.

(Hint: Establish the following Lemma: If U is a nonempty
open and closed subset of a compact, perfect, totally disconnected metric space, and if k is a positive integer, then U is
the union of k nonempty disjoint open sets.)

10
QUOTIENT SPACES

<u>Definition</u>. Let X be a set. If $\mathcal{E}$ is an equivalence rela-
tion on X we let $X/\mathcal{E}$ denote the set of equivalence classes of $\mathcal{E}$,
and we let $\varphi : X \to X/\mathcal{E}$ be the natural function defined by $x \in \varphi(x)$
for all $x \in X$. If X is a topological space then the <u>quotient
topology</u> on $X/\mathcal{E}$ is obtained by calling a subset V of $X/\mathcal{E}$ open if
and only if $\varphi^{-1}(V)$ is open in X. Relative to the quotient topology, $X/\mathcal{E}$ is a <u>quotient space</u> of X.

<u>Proposition 10.1</u>. If X is a space and $\mathcal{E}$ is an equivalence
relation on X then the open sets of $X/\mathcal{E}$ form a topology and the
natural function $\varphi : X \to X/\mathcal{E}$ is continuous. Moreover, a subset
K of $X/\mathcal{E}$ is closed if and only if $\varphi^{-1}(K)$ is closed.

<u>Examples</u>.

(1) If X and Y are spaces then X is homeomorphic to a quotient space of $X \times Y$.

(2) Let X be a space and let $\square \neq A \subset X$. If
$$\mathcal{E}(A) = (A \times A) \cup \{(x, x) : x \in X\}$$
then $X/\mathcal{E}(A)$ is a quotient space of X which "identifies A with a
point." If A is either open or closed then $\varphi|(X - A)$ is a homeo-
morphism.

(3) In a space X let $\mathcal{E}$ be the equivalence relation whose
elements are the components of X. Then $X/\mathcal{E}$ is totally disconnected

<u>Theorem 77</u>. Let X and Y be spaces and suppose $f : X \to Y$ is
a continuous surjection which is either open or closed. Let $\mathcal{E}(f)$
denote the equivalence relation on X defined by

$(a, b) \in \delta(f)$ if and only if $f(a) = f(b)$.
Then Y and $X/\delta(f)$ are homeomorphic.

Theorem 78. If X and Y are spaces, δ is an equivalence
relation on X, and $f : X/\delta \to Y$ is a function, then f is continuous if and only if $f\varphi : X \to Y$ is continuous.

Examples.

(4) The n-sphere S^n is homeomorphic to the quotient space
formed from I^n by identifying the bounding $(n - 1)$-sphere of I^n
with a point.

(5) If X is a space then the <u>cone over</u> X, denoted $Cn(X)$,
is the quotient space formed from $X \times [0, 1]$ by identifying
$X \times \{1\}$ with a point. If $f : X \to Y$ is continuous then the mapping $(x, t) \to (f(x), t)$ induces a mapping from $Cn(X)$ to $Cn(Y)$.
Prove that $Cn(S^n)$ is homeomorphic to I^{n+1}.

Definition. An equivalence relation δ on a space X is
<u>closed</u> if δ is a closed subset of $X \times X$.

Theorem 79. Let X be a space and suppose δ is an equivalence relation on X. If X/δ is a Hausdorff space then δ is
closed. If δ is closed and $\varphi : X \to X/\delta$ is open, then X/δ is a
Hausdorff space. If X is a compact Hausdorff space then X/δ is
a Hausdorff space if and only if δ is closed.

(<u>Hint</u>: For the last part, let $\varphi \times \varphi$ denote the mapping
$X \times X \to (X/\delta) \times (X/\delta)$ induced by φ and show that $\varphi \times \varphi$ is a
closed mapping.)

Definition. Let X and Y be disjoint topological spaces.
The <u>topological sum</u> of X and Y, denoted $X + Y$, is the set $X \cup Y$
topologized in the following way: a subset U of $X + Y$ is open
provided $U \cap X$ and $U \cap Y$ are open subsets of X and Y, respectively.

Example.

(6)   Verify that the open sets of X + Y form a topology.
Show that a subset F of X + Y is closed if and only if F ∩ Y
and F ∩ X are closed subsets of X and Y, respectively.

Definition.   Let X and Y be disjoint spaces, let A be a
subset of X, and suppose f : A → Y is a mapping.   Let δ(f) be
the equivalence relation on X + Y defined by (x, f(x)) ∈ δ(f)
for all x ∈ A.   Then

$$X \cup_f Y = (X + Y)/\delta(f)$$

is the adjunction of X to Y by f.

Examples.

(7)   If X is a space and □ ≠ A ⊂ X, then X/δ(A) is homeomorphic to the adjunction of X to a singleton space.   In particular, Cn(X) is the adjunction of X × [0, 1] to a singleton.

(8)   If X is a space let S(X) denote the space obtained
from X × [-1, 1] by identifying X × {1} and X × {-1} with distinct points.   The space S(X) is the suspension of X.   Note
that S(X) is homeomorphic to the adjunction of X × [-1, 1] with
a discrete two-point space.   Moreover, S(X) and Cn(X)/δ(X × {0})
are homeomorphic.   Finally, S(S^n) and S^{n+1} are homeomorphic.

Proposition 10.2.   If X and Y are disjoint spaces, A is a
closed subset of X, f : A → Y is a mapping, and ψ : X + Y → X $\cup_f$ Y
is the natural mapping, then ψ|Y and ψ|(X - A) are homeomor-
phisms.

11
NETS AND COMPACTNESS

Earlier we saw that the topology of a metric space or a
first countable space can be completely described in terms of
sequences (Theorem 11 and the Example 8 of Chapter 7), but that
sequences are inadequate to describe the topologies of all spaces
(e. g., the space $\mathcal{O}(\Omega)$, cf. Example 46 of Chapter 1).   In the present chapter we study a generalization of the notion of a sequence--
the concept of net--which overcomes this defect.

Definition.   A partially ordered set (D, $\leq$) is called a
directed set if for each x, y $\in$ D there exists z $\in$ D such that
x $\leq$ z and y $\leq$ z.

Remark.   Any simply ordered set is directed.   If X is a
space, x $\in$ X, and $\mathcal{N}_x$ is the family of all neighborhoods of x,
then $(\mathcal{N}_x, \supset)$ is directed.

Definition.   A net is a function whose domain is a directed
set.   If x is a net with domain D then x is eventually in the
set T provided there exists d(T) $\in$ D such that x(d) $\in$ T for all
d > d(T), and x is frequently in T if for each d $\in$ D there exists
e > d such that x(e) $\in$ T.   A net x in a space X converges to the
element p $\in$ X provided x is eventually in each neighborhood of
p.   If x converges to p we write lim x = p or x $\rightarrow$ p.   The net
x clusters to p (or, p is a cluster point of x) provided x is
frequently in each neighborhood of p.

Remark.   It is apparent that any sequence is a net and that
a sequence converges or clusters if and only if it converges or
clusters as a net.

65

Definition. Let x : (D, ≤) → S be a net. If (E, ≤) is a
directed set, if y : E → D is an order-preserving function
(i. e., if e_1 ≤ e_2 in E then $y(e_1)$ ≤ $y(e_2)$), and if for each
d_0 ∈ D it follows that y is eventually in $\{d ∈ D : d_0 ≤ d\}$,
then xy : E → S is a subnet of x.

Examples.

(1) Every subsequence of a given sequence is also a subnet
of that sequence. However it does not follow that every subnet
of a sequence is a subsequence.

(2) If X is a space and p ∈ Lp(X) then there exists a net
in X - $\{p\}$ which converges to p.

Theorem 80. Let X be a space, p ∈ X, and x a net in X.
Then p is a cluster point of x if and only if some subnet of x
converges to p.

Theorem 81. Suppose X is a space, p ∈ X, and A ⊂ X. Then
p ∈ Ā if and only if some net in A converges to p. A subset U
of X is open if and only if each net which converges to an element of U is eventually in U.

Proposition 11.1. Let X and Y be spaces, f : X → Y a function, and p ∈ X. Then f is continuous at p if and only if for
each net x → p it follows that fx → f(p).

Theorem 82. If X is a space, then the following statements
are equivalent.

(i) The space X is connected.

(ii) If A is a nonempty, closed proper subset of X, then
there exists a net in X - A converging to an element of A.

(iii) If A is a nonempty, open proper subset of X, then
there exists a net in A converging to an element of X - A.

(iv) If A is a nonempty proper subset of X, then either
there is a net in A which converges to an element of X - A, or

there exists a net in X - A which converges to an element of A.

Theorem 83. If X is a space then the following statements
are equivalent.

(i)   The space X is compact.

(ii)   Each net in X has a convergent subnet.

(iii)   Each net in X has a cluster point.

Theorem 84. Consider the following statements about a
space X.

(i)   For each pair of distinct elements of X there exists
a net in X which converges to precisely one of the elements.

(ii)   If a and b are distinct elements of X then there exists
a net which converges to a and does not converge to b.

(iii)   No net in X converges to more than one element.

Then X is a T_0 space if and only if (i) is true; X is a
T_1 space if and only if (ii) is true; and X is a T_2 space if and
only if (iii) is true.

Definition. A net x in the set S is a universal net (more
precisely, x is universal in S) provided for each $A \subset S$ either
x is eventually in A or x is eventually in S - A.

Examples.

(3)   An eventually constant net is universal. The net
$x(n) = n$ in $\underset{\sim}{N}$ is not universal.

(4)   If $T \subset S$ and x is a net universal in T, then x is
universal in S.

Proposition 11.2. A universal net in a topological space
converges to each of its cluster points.

Proposition 11.3. If S and T are sets, x is a net which
is universal in S, and $f : S \to T$ is a function, then fx is universal in T.

Theorem 85. If x is a net in the set S then x has a subnet which is universal in S.

[Warning: This requires a sophisticated application of the Axiom of Choice (see Chapter 0). A possible argument--but not the only one--begins as follows. There exists a family $\mathcal{C}$ of subsets of S which is maximal with respect to satisfying these conditions: (1) if $\mathcal{J}$ is a finite subfamily of $\mathcal{C}$ then $\cap \mathcal{J} \in \mathcal{C}$; (2) if $A \in \mathcal{C}$ then x is frequently in A. If $x : D \to S$, then let $E = \{(A, d) : A \in \mathcal{C}, d \in D, \underline{\text{and}} \ x(d) \in A\}$ and define $y : E \to D$ by $y((A, d)) = d$. Consider the subnet xy.]

Theorem 86. (Tychonoff.) The product of a family of compact spaces is compact.

While the Tychonoff theorem is a consequence of Theorem 85, there are at least two other proofs. One of these is dependent on the next result, which is usually called Alexander's Lemma.

Theorem 87. Let S be a set and let $\mathcal{B}$ be a family of subsets of S. Then S is compact with respect to $\mathcal{J}(\mathcal{B})$ if and only if each cover of S by members of $\mathcal{B}$ has a finite subcover.

(Hint: If S is not compact then there exists $\mathcal{U} \subset \mathcal{J}(\mathcal{B})$ which is maximal with respect to covering S and having no finite sub-cover. If $B_1, \ldots, B_n \in \mathcal{B}$ and if $B_1 \cap \cdots \cap B_n \subset U \in \mathcal{U}$, then some $B_i \in \mathcal{U}$. Evidently $\mathcal{B} \cap \mathcal{U}$ (and hence $\mathcal{U}$) cannot cover S.)

Problem. Use Theorem 87 to prove Theorem 86.

12
EMBEDDING AND METRIZATION

If X and Y are spaces and if there exists a homeomorphism
h : X → Y, then h may be called an _embedding_. If we identify X
with h(X), then we say that X is _embedded_ in Y. Thus we can re-
gard $\underline{R}$ as being embedded in $\underline{R}^2$ via the homeomorphism t → (t, 0),
and every subset of a space is trivially embedded via the iden-
tity mapping. In a number of instances the technique of embedding
is of great importance. We have already seen (Corollary 65.1)
that any metric space can be embedded in some complete metric
space. In fact, in that case the embedding was an isometry. In
this chapter we study three more important embedding theorems.
First it is helpful to prove the following remarkable charac-
terization of normal spaces.

Theorem 88. (Urysohn's Lemma.) A space X is normal if and
only if for each pair of disjoint closed subsets F and K, there
exists a mapping f : X → [0, 1] such that f(x) = 0 for each
x ∈ F, and f(x) = 1 for each x ∈ K.

(Hint: For each dyadic rational r (i. e., each r = $p/2^q$
where p, q ∈ $\underline{Z}$) such that $0 \le r \le 1$, find an open set U(r) such
that, if r < s, then $F \subset U(r) \subset \overline{U(r)} \subset U(s) \subset X - K$.)

Definition. The product space I^N, i. e., the denumerable
product of copies of I = [0, 1], is called the _Hilbert cube_.

Remark. The Hilbert cube is a compact metrizable space.

Theorem 89. (Urysohn.) Any second countable T_3 space can

69

be embedded in the Hilbert cube. Consequently, a second countable space is metrizable if and only if it is a T_3 space.

   In the absence of second countability, the metrization
problem is more complicated and we do not treat it here. However, the question of embedding a space in some sort of cube
remains. For nonmetrizable spaces such a cube would necessarily
have an uncountable family of coordinate intervals.

   Definition. A space X is completely regular provided, for
each closed subset F of X and each p $\in$ X - F, there exists a
mapping f : X $\to$ [0, 1] such that f(p) = 0 and f(x) = 1 for each
x $\in$ F.

   A completely regular T_1 space is called a Tychonoff space.

   Examples.
   (1) Discrete and indiscrete spaces are completely regular.
   (2) A cofinite space is completely regular if and only if
it is finite.

   Proposition 12.1. A T_4 space is a Tychonoff space. A
completely regular space is regular. Every subspace of a completely regular space is completely regular, and consequently
there exist Tychonoff spaces which are not normal.

   Definition. If A is a nonempty set, then the space I^A,
i. e., the product of #(A)-many copies of I, is called a cube.

   Theorem 90. Every Tychonoff space can be embedded in some
cube.

   (Hint: If X is a Tychonoff space, let $\mathcal{F}$ denote the family
of all mappings f : X $\to$ [0, 1]. Define h : X $\to$ $I^{\mathcal{F}}$ by $\pi_f h$ = f.)

   Corollary 90.1. A space is a Tychonoff space if and only
if it can be embedded in a compact Hausdorff space.

Definition. Any space of the form 2^A, i. e., the product of a family of discrete two-point spaces, is called a Cantor space.

Recall that according to Theorem 76 the space $\underset{\sim}{C}$ is a Cantor space, and therefore any compact, totally disconnected metric space can be embedded as a closed subset of $2^{\underset{\sim}{N}}$.

Theorem 91. A compact, totally disconnected Hausdorff space can be embedded in some Cantor space.

We give an example of a T_3 space which is not completely regular. Proposition 12.2 is useful in developing that example.

Proposition 12.2. If X is a Tychonoff space and if X is always closed when embedded as a subset of a T_3 space, then X is compact.

Example.

(3) For each $n = 1, 2, \ldots$ let P_n be a homeomorph of the space S of Example 7 of Chapter 6. In each P_n let $X_n = \{(x, \omega) : x < \Omega\}$ and let $Y_n = \{(\Omega, y) : y < \omega\}$. Let P_∞ be the topological sum of the spaces Y_n, i. e., a subset U of P_∞ is open if $U \cap P_n$ is open for each n. We form a quotient space T from P_∞ by the following identifications: if n is odd then X_n and X_{n+1} are identified in the natural way, but if n is even then Y_n and Y_{n+1} are so identified. Now adjoin a new element ξ to T. The set $\tilde{T} = T \cup \{\xi\}$ is topologized as follows: a base for the topology of $\tilde{T}$ consists of all open subsets of T together with all sets of the form $\cup \{P_k : k \geq n\} \cup \{\xi\}$. It can be proved that $\tilde{T}$ is a T_3 space which is not compact. Moreover, whenever $\tilde{T}$ is embedded as a subset of a T_3 space then $\tilde{T}$ is closed.

13
LOCALLY COMPACT SPACES

Definition. If X is a space and $p \in X$, then X is <u>locally compact</u> at p provided p has a compact neighborhood. If X is locally compact at each of its elements, then X is <u>locally</u> <u>compact</u>.

Examples.

(1) If a space is compact, discrete, or Euclidean, then it is locally compact.

(2) The spaces $\underset{\sim}{Q}$ and $(\underset{\sim}{R}, \mathcal{J}_r)$ are not locally compact.

Proposition 13.1. Closed subspaces of locally compact spaces are locally compact. Continuous open surjections preserve local compactness.

Theorem 92. A locally compact Hausdorff space is completely regular.

Corollary 92.1. A Hausdorff space X is locally compact if and only if, for each $p \in X$, each neighborhood of p contains a compact neighborhood of p.

Corollary 92.2. An open subset of a locally compact Hausdorff space is locally compact in its relative topology.

Example.

(3) The space S of Example 6 of Chapter 6 is a locally compact Hausdorff space which is not normal.

Theorem 93. Let X be a locally compact Hausdorff space,

let F and K be disjoint closed subsets of X, and suppose that K is compact. Then there exists a mapping $f : X \to [0, 1]$ such that $f(x) = 1$ for each $x \in F$, and $f(x) = 0$ for each $x \in K$.

Theorem 94. If $\mathcal{X}$ is a family of spaces then $\Pi \mathcal{X}$ is locally compact if and only if each $X \in \mathcal{X}$ is locally compact and all but a finite number of members of $\mathcal{X}$ are compact.

Theorem 95. (Baire-Moore.) No locally compact Hausdorff space is meager.

Theorem 96. Let X be a locally compact Hausdorff space and let $A \subset X$. Then A is a closed set if and only if $A \cap K$ is compact, for each compact subset K of X.

Theorem 97. Let X be a locally compact Hausdorff space and suppose $Y \subset X$. Then Y is locally compact in its relative topology if and only if there exists a closed set C and an open set G such that $Y = G \cap C$.

Definition. Let X be a space which is not compact and let p be an object which is not a member of X. Let $X^* = X \cup \{p\}$ be topologized by calling a subset V of X^* open, provided (1) V is an open subset of X or (2) $p \in V$ and $X - V$ is closed and compact. The space X^* is called the one-point compactification of X.

Theorem 98. If X is a space which is not compact, then X^* is a compact space and X is embedded as a dense open subset of X^*. Moreover, if Y is a compact space and if X can be embedded in Y as a dense open subset whose complement is a singleton, then X^* and Y are homeomorphic.

Examples.

(4) The spaces $\underline{R}^*$ and S^1 are homeomorphic. More generally, $(\underline{R}^n)^*$ and S^n are homeomorphic.

(5) The space $\underset{\sim}{N}$* is homeomorphic to $\{x \in \underset{\sim}{R} : x = 0 \text{ or } x = 1/n \text{ for some } n = 1, 2, \ldots\}$.

(6) The space $\mathcal{O}(\Omega)$ is the one-point compactification of $\mathcal{O}(\Omega) - \{\Omega\}$.

(7) If $X = \{x \in \underset{\sim}{R}^2 : 1 \leq x_1^2 + x_2^2 < 2\}$ then X* is a 2-cell.

(8) If X is a noncompact T_1 space then X* is a T_1 space.

Theorem 99. If X is a noncompact space then X* is a Hausdorff space if and only if X is a locally compact Hausdorff space.

Theorem 100. If X is a locally compact, noncompact, secondcountable Hausdorff space, then X* is metrizable.

Definition. If X is a space then a compactification of X is a pair (Y, f) where Y is a compact space, f is an embedding of X into Y, and f(X) is dense in Y.

Obviously, if X is not compact and i is the identity mapping, then (X*, i) is a compactification in this sense. However, it is easy to see that there are a great many ways to embed most noncompact spaces in a compact space. (Consider the space $]0, 1[$, for example.) The one-point compactification is merely the simplest of these.

Theorem 101. A Hausdorff space X is locally compact if and only if for each Hausdorff compactification (Y, f) of X, the set f(X) is an open subset of Y.

Remark. According to Corollary 90.1, every Tychonoff space has a Hausdorff compactification. If X is a Tychonoff space and $h : X \to I^{\mathcal{J}}$ is the embedding of Theorem 90, let $\beta(X) = \overline{h(X)}$. Then $\beta(X)$ is called the Stone-Cech compactification of X.

Theorem 102. Let X be a Tychonoff space and $h : X \to \beta(X)$ the embedding of Theorem 90. If $g : X \to I$ is a mapping, then

gh^{-1} admits a continuous extension to $\beta(X)$. Conversely, if
(Y, f) is a Hausdorff compactification of X and if, for each
mapping g : X → I, it follows that gf^{-1} has a continuous extension to Y, then Y and $\beta(X)$ are homeomorphic.

If X is an arbitrary T_1 space, let w(X) denote the set of
all families of closed subsets of X which are maximal with respect to having the f. i. p. [In particular, the family of all
closed sets containing a fixed element of X is a member of w(X)].
For each subset A of X let

$$\widehat{A} = \{a \in w(X) : \underline{\text{there}} \ \underline{\text{exists}} \ F \in a \ \underline{\text{and}} \ F \subset A\}.$$

Theorem 103. If X is a T_1 space then $\{\widehat{U} :$ U is an open
subset of X} is a base for a topology on w(X). Moreover, relative to that topology, w(X) is a compactification of X.

The compactification w(X) is called the Wallman compactification of X.

Theorem 104. If X is a T_4 space then w(X) and $\beta(X)$ are
homeomorphic.

Examples.
(9) $(\mathcal{O}(\Omega) - \{\Omega\})^* = \beta(\mathcal{O}(\Omega) - \{\Omega\}) = \mathcal{O}(\Omega).$
(10) Every ordered space admits a compactification which is
an ordered space.

Definition. A continuum is a compact, connected Hausdorff space.

Examples.

(1) The spaces $[0, 1]$, I^n, and S^n are continua.

(2) An ordered space S is a continuum if and only if (1) for each a, b $\in$ S with a $<$ b there exists c $\in$ S such that a $<$ c $<$ b, and (2) each nonempty subset of S has a least upper bound and a greatest lower bound.

Proposition 14.1. If X is a continuum, Y is a Hausdorff space, and f : X $\to$ Y is a continuous surjection, then Y is a continuum. The product of a family of continua is a continuum. The adjunction of two continua by a closed set is a continuum.

Definition. If X is a space and Y is a nonempty subset of X which is a continuum in its relative topology, then Y is a subcontinuum of X.

Definition. A family $\mathcal{A}$ of sets is nested if, for each A, B $\in \mathcal{A}$, either A $\subset$ B or B $\subset$ A.

That is, $\mathcal{A}$ is nested provided $\mathcal{A}$ is simply ordered by the inclusion relation.

Theorem 105. If $\mathcal{A}$ is a nested family of subcontinua of some space, then $\bigcap \mathcal{A}$ is a continuum.

Definition. If X is a space and A is a nonempty subset of

X, then a subcontinuum K of X is <u>irreducible about</u> A provided
K ⊃ A and no proper subcontinuum of K contains A.

<u>Theorem 106</u>. If X is a continuum and A is a nonempty sub-
set of X, then X contains a subcontinuum which is irreducible
about A.

<u>Definition</u>. Suppose A and B are nonempty disjoint subsets
of a space X. A subcontinuum K of X is <u>irreducible from</u> A <u>to</u> B
if K meets both A and B and no proper subcontinuum of K meets
both A and B.

<u>Theorem 107</u>. If X is a continuum and A and B are nonempty
disjoint closed subsets of X, then X contains a subcontinuum
which is irreducible from A to B.

<u>Theorem 108</u>. Let X be a compact Hausdorff space, and sup-
pose $\mathcal{F}$ is a family of closed subsets of X with the property that
if $F_1, \ldots, F_n$ are members of $\mathcal{F}$, then there exists $F_0 \in \mathcal{F}$ such
that $F_0 \subset F_1 \cap F_2 \cap \cdots \cap F_n$. If U is an open set containing
$\cap \mathcal{F}$ then there exists $F \in \mathcal{F}$ such that $F \subset U$.

<u>Theorem 109</u>. Let X be a compact Hausdorff space, and sup-
pose A and B are disjoint closed subsets of X such that no subcontinuum of X meets both A and B. Then there is a decomposition
X = M ∪ N, where M and N are disjoint closed sets, A ⊂ M, and
B ⊂ N.

<u>Remark</u>. Compare Theorem 109 with Theorem 72.

<u>Theorem 110</u>. Let X be a Hausdorff space, let A and B be
disjoint closed subsets of X, and suppose that K is a subcontinuum of X which is irreducible from A to B. Then the sets
K - (A ∪ B), K - A, and K - B are connected. Moreover, K ∩ A
and K ∩ B are subsets of $\overline{K - (A \cup B)}$.

Theorem 111. If X is a continuum, Y is a Hausdorff space,
and f : X → Y is a continuous surjection, then X contains a
subcontinuum K which is minimal relative to the property f(K) =
Y.

Definition. Let X be a space and p ∈ X. A set Q of the
form
$$Q = \cap \{V : p \in V, V \text{ is closed and } V \text{ is open}\}$$
is a quasi component of X.

Example.
(3) In discrete spaces the quasi components are singletons.
A connected space is its only quasi component.

Proposition 14.2. The quasi components of X are disjoint
closed sets which cover X. Each component of X is a subset of
some quasi component of X.

Example.
(4) A quasi component of a space is not necessarily a
component. For each $n \in \underline{N}$ let
$$L_n = \{(2^{-n}, y) \in \underline{R}^2 : 0 \le y \le 1\},$$
let x = (0, 0), and let y = (0, 1). Let
$$X = \{x, y\} \cup \bigcup_{n=0}^{\infty} \{L_n\}$$
with the relative topology inherited from $\underline{R}^2$. The component of
X which contains x is {x}, but the quasi component which contains
x is {x, y}.

Theorem 112. In a compact Hausdorff space the components
and quasi components are identical.

·Theorem 113. Each compact quasi component of a locally
compact Hausdorff space is a component.

Theorem 114. If K is a component of a compact Hausdorff

space and U is an open set containing K, then there exists an open set V such that $K \subset V \subset U$ and $\partial V = \square$.

Theorem 115. If U is a nonempty proper open subset of a continuum and if K is a component of U, then $K \cap \partial U \neq \square$.

Theorem 116. (Sierpinski.) No continuum is the union of a countable (> 1) family of disjoint, nonempty closed sets.

(Hint: If $X = \bigcup_{n=1}^{\infty} \{A_n\}$ where the A_n's are closed and disjoint, obtain a sequence of subcontinua K_n such that $K_{n+1} \subset K_n$ and $K_n \cap A_n = \square$.)

15

CUTPOINTS AND ARCS

An important problem of topology is to recognize the n-cells and n-spheres in terms of purely topological properties. We will solve this problem only for the simplest case, n = 1.

Definition. Let A, B, and S be subsets of a space X. If X - S = M $\cup$ N where A $\subset$ M, B $\subset$ N, and M|N, then S separates A and B. A set which separates two nonempty subsets of X is called a separator of X. If X is connected, p $\in$ X, and if {p} is a separator of X, then p is a cutpoint of X.

Examples.

(1) A space X is connected if and only if $\square$ is not a separator of X.

(2) Every nonempty bounded subset of $\underset{\sim}{R}$ is a separator of $\underset{\sim}{R}$, and hence every element of $\underset{\sim}{R}$ is a cutpoint.

(3) The set S^n is a separator of $\underset{\sim}{R}^{n+1}$, for each n = 0, 1, ...

(4) If n > 1 then $\underset{\sim}{R}^n$ has no cutpoints.

(5) Indiscrete and infinite cofinite spaces have no cutpoints.

Theorem 117. If X is a connected T_1 space and p $\in$ X, then the following statements are equivalent.

(i) p is a cutpoint of X.

(ii) X - {p} = U $\cup$ V, where U and V are disjoint open sets, $\overline{U}$ = U $\cup$ {p}, $\overline{V}$ = V $\cup$ {p}, and the sets $\overline{U}$ and $\overline{V}$ are connected.

(iii) X = M $\cup$ N, where M and N are nondegenerate closed and connected sets such that M $\cap$ N = {p}.

Theorem 118. (R. L. Moore.) A nondegenerate continuum has
at least two noncutpoints.

(Hint: Suppose that X is a continuum, $p \in X$, and each
$x \in X - \{p\}$ is a cutpoint. Thus $X = M_x \cup N_x$ where M_x and N_x are
nondegenerate subcontinua, $p \in M_x$, and $M_x \cap N_x = \{x\}$.)

Definition. A continuum is $\underline{straight}$ if it has exactly two
noncutpoints.

Examples.

(6) The unit interval $[0, 1]$ is straight.

(7) The 2-cell I^2, ordered lexicographically, is a straight
continuum with respect to the order topology.

Theorem 119. If X is a straight continuum and x is a cutpoint of X, then $X - \{x\}$ has exactly two components, each of
which contains a noncutpoint of X.

Notation. Let X be a straight continuum with noncutpoints
0 and 1. If $x \in X - \{0, 1\}$, write $X = L_x \cup M_x$ where L_x and M_x
are nondegenerate subcontinua of X, $L_x - \{x\}$ is the component of
$X - \{x\}$ which contains 0, and $M_x - \{x\}$ is the component of $X - \{x\}$
which contains 1. Moreover, write $L_0 = \{0\}$, $M_0 = X = L_1$, and
$M_1 = \{1\}$. Define a relation $\leq$ on X by $x \leq y$ if and only if
$y \in M_x$.

Proposition 15.1. If X is a straight continuum, then $L_x = \{y \in X : y \leq x\}$ and $M_x = \{y \in X : x \leq y\}$.

Theorem 120. If X is a straight continuum, then $\leq$ is a
simple order and the order topology and the given topology are
identical. Moreover, as an ordered set, X satisfies the Dedekind property.

Theorem 121. Let C be a countable ordered set. Suppose

(1) C has no first element and no last element, and (2) for
each a, b ∈ C with a < b, there exists c ∈ C such that a < c < b.
Then there exists an order-preserving bijection φ : C → Q̰.

   Definition. An arc is a space which is homeomorphic to
[0, 1].

   Theorem 122. A space is an arc if and only if it is a
separable straight continuum.

   Theorem 123. If X is a continuum and if each nondegenerate
doubleton subset is a separator of X, then X has no cutpoints.

   Theorem 124. Let X be a continuum each of whose nondegenerate doubleton subsets is a separator. If D is a nondegenerate
doubleton subset and X - D = P ∪ Q, where P and Q are nonempty
separated sets, then P ∪ D is a straight continuum.

   Definition. A simple closed curve is a space which is
homeomorphic to S^1.

   Corollary 124.1. A space is a simple closed curve if and
only if it is a separable continuum in which each nondegenerate
doubleton subset is a separator.

16
INDECOMPOSABLE CONTINUA[1]

Arcs and simple closed curves are continua of an especially simple, well-behaved character. One's intuition accepts most of their properties without hesitation, and intuition is a reliable guide in predicting those properties. In this chapter we consider a class of continua of a sharply different nature, whose properties are utterly pathological, and which, to the untrained intuition, may seem unbelievable.

Definition. A continuum is <u>indecomposable</u> if it is nondegenerate and if it is not the union of two of its proper subcontinua.

A little reflection will persuade the reader that almost any continuum which comes to mind—certainly any continuum so far considered in this book—fails to satisfy the definition of indecomposability. A skeptic might even question whether any such objects exist. We shall settle the question of existence in the affirmative, but before doing so it is helpful to establish a few preliminary results.

Theorem 125. No subcontinuum of an indecomposable continuum is a separator.

Theorem 126. A nondegenerate continuum is indecomposable if and only if each of its connected subsets is either dense or nowhere dense.

83

Corollary 126.1.   A nondegenerate continuum is indecomposable if and only if each of its proper subcontinua is nowhere dense.

Definition.   If X is a continuum and $p \in X$, then the set of all $x \in X$ such that $\{p, x\}$ is contained in a proper subcontinuum of X is called a composant of X.

Examples.

(1)   The composants of a continuum are connected sets which cover the continuum.

(2)   The continuum $I = [0, 1]$ has three composants, and S^1 has one composant.

Theorem 127.   A composant of a continuum is a dense subset.

Theorem 128.   Each composant of a nondegenerate metrizable continuum is the union of a countable family of proper subcontinua.

Theorem 129.   The composants of an indecomposable continuum are mutually disjoint.

Theorem 130.   An indecomposable metrizable continuum has uncountably many composants.

Theorem 131.   A metrizable continuum X is indecomposable if and only if there exist three distinct elements of X such that no proper subcontinuum of X contains two of them.

Theorem 132.   A metrizable continuum is indecomposable if and only if it contains a composant with empty interior.

Example.

(3)   In $\underset{\sim}{R}^2$ let

$$\mathcal{K} = \{(x, 0) : x \in \underset{\sim}{\mathcal{Q}}\}$$

and let A denote the union of all semicircles with center (1/2, 0), which contain an element of $\mathcal{X}$, and which lie in the upper half-plane. For each n = 1, 2, ... let B_n denote the union of all semicircles with center $(5/(2 \cdot 3^n), 0)$, which contain an element $(x, 0) \in \mathcal{X}$ such that $2/3^n \le x \le 1/3^{n-1}$, and which lie in the lower half-plane. Let

$$K = A \cup \bigcup_{n=1}^{\infty} \{B_n\}.$$

The composant of K determined by (0, 0) is a bijective continuous image of $[0, \infty[$ and every other composant is a bijective continuous image of $\underset{\sim}{R}$. It follows from Theorem 132 that K is indecomposable. (See Figure 2.)

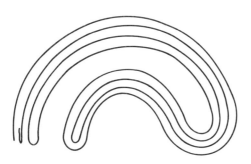

FIGURE 2

FOOTNOTE

[1]This chapter is independent of the remainder of the book and may be omitted.

Definition. If X is a space and $p \in X$, then X is <u>locally</u> <u>connected</u> at p provided each neighborhood of p contains a connected neighborhood of p. If X is locally connected at each of its elements, then X is <u>locally connected</u>.

Examples.

(1) Discrete, indiscrete, and cofinite spaces are locally connected.

(2) Euclidean spaces are locally connected.

(3) Neither $\underset{\sim}{Q}$ nor $(\underset{\sim}{R}, \mathcal{J}_r)$ is locally connected at any element.

(4) No indecomposable continuum is locally connected.

Proposition 17.1. Open subspaces of locally connected spaces are locally connected. Continuous open surjections preserve local connectedness.

Proposition 17.2. The space X is locally connected if and only if each neighborhood of each element p of X contains a connected open neighborhood of p.

Examples.

(5) Let $Y_{-1} = \{(x, 0) \in \underset{\sim}{R}^2 : 0 \leq x \leq 1$, and for each $n \in \underset{\sim}{N}$ let $Y_n = \{(2^{-n}, y) \in \underset{\sim}{R}^2 : 0 \leq y \leq 1\}$. The space

$$\bigcup_{n=-1}^{\infty} \{Y_n\}$$

is locally connected. If $Y_{-2} = \{(0, y) : 0 < y \leq 1\}$, then the space

86

$$\overset{\infty}{\underset{n=-2}{\cup}} \{Y_n\}$$

fails to be locally connected at each element of Y_{-2} but is locally connected at all other elements.

(6) The space

$$B \cup \overset{\infty}{\underset{n=1}{\cup}} \{A_n\}$$

of Example 12 of Chapter 2 is locally connected at each element
not in B and fails to be locally connected at each element of B.

Theorem 133. A space is locally connected if and only if
each component of each open set is open.

Corollary 133.1. A compact and locally connected space has
only finitely many components.

Corollary 133.2. If X is a connected and locally connected
space, if A is a closed subset of X, and if C is a component of
X - A, then $\overline{C} \cap A \neq \square$.

Corollary 133.3. Continuous closed surjections preserve
local connectedness.

Theorem 134. A metric space X is locally connected at the
element p of X if and only if, for each $\varepsilon > 0$, there exists
$\delta > 0$ such that if $x \in X$ and $\rho(x, p) < \delta$, then there exists a
connected set C such that $\{p, x\} \subset C$ and $\text{diam}(C) < \varepsilon$.

Theorem 135. Let $\mathcal{X}$ be a family of spaces. The space $\Pi\mathcal{X}$
is locally connected if and only if each member of $\mathcal{X}$ is locally
connected and all but a finite subfamily of the members of $\mathcal{X}$ are
connected.

Theorem 136. In a locally connected space the components
and quasi components are identical.

Theorem 137. Let X be a locally compact, connected Hausdorff

space. Then X is locally connected if and only if, for each
compact subset K and each open set U which contains K, all but
a finite number of the components of X - K are contained in U.

Definition. A metric space (X, ρ) is <u>uniformly locally</u>
<u>connected</u> provided for each $\epsilon > 0$ there exists $\delta > 0$ such that
if x, y $\in$ X and $\rho(x, y) < \delta$, then there exists a connected set
C such that $\{x, y\} \subset C$ and diam(C) < ϵ.

Examples.

(7) Let H = $\{2^{-n} : n \in \underset{\sim}{N}\}$ with the relative topology inherited from $\underset{\sim}{R}$. Since H is discrete, it is locally connected.
However, relative to the Euclidean metric, H is not uniformly
locally connected.

(8) A uniformly locally connected metric space is locally
connected.

We will show that in a compact metric space the notions of
local connectivity and uniform local connectivity are equivalent.
The following important theorem, called the <u>Lebesgue Lemma</u>, is
a helpful preliminary result.

Theorem 138. If X is a compact metric space and $\mathcal{U}$ is a
finite open cover of X, then there exists a real number $\delta(\mathcal{U}) > 0$
such that if A $\subset$ X and diam(A) $< \delta(\mathcal{U})$, then A $\subset$ U for some U $\in \mathcal{U}$.

Theorem 139. A compact, locally connected metric space is
uniformly locally connected.

Theorem 140. If X is a locally connected, complete metric space and if a and b are distinct elements lying in the same component of X, then there exists a mapping $f : [0, 1] \to X$ such that $f(0) = a$ and $f(1) = b$.

(**Hint**: Obtain a simple chain of connected open sets from a to b, say $\{U_1, \ldots, U_n\}$, where $\mathrm{diam}(U_i) < 1$ for each $i = 1, \ldots, n$. Choose $x_0 = a$, $x_i \in U_i \cap U_{i+1}$, $x_n = b$, and let $f(i/n) = a$.)

Definition. A **Peano continuum** is a locally connected, metrizable continuum.

Theorem 141. If X is a compact, second countable Hausdorff space, Y is a Hausdorff space, and $f : X \to Y$ is a continuous surjection, then Y is compact and second countable. Consequently, if $X = [0, 1]$ then Y is a Peano continuum.

Theorem 142. If Y is a compact metric space, then there exists a closed subset K of $\mathcal{C}$ and a continuous surjection $f : K \to Y$.

(**Hint**: Let $\{U_0, U_1, \ldots\}$ be a countable base for Y, for each n let $A_0^n = \overline{U}_n$, $A_1^n = X - U_n$, and for each $t \in 2^{\mathbb{N}}$ let $\Phi(t) = \bigcap_{n=0}^{\infty} \{A_{t_n}^n\}$. Then $\Phi(t)$ either is empty or is a singleton.)

Definition. If X is a space, $Y \subset X$, and $r : X \to Y$ is a mapping such that $r(y) = y$ for each $y \in Y$, then r is a **retraction** and Y is a **retract** of X.

Examples.

(1) Every space is a retract of itself. If $x \in X$ then
$\{x\}$ is a retract of X.

(2) If $\square \neq Y \subset X$ and X is a discrete space, then Y is a
retract of X.

(3) S^n is a retract of $\underset{\sim}{R}^{n+1} - \{0\}$.

Proposition 18.1. Any retract of a Hausdorff space is a
closed subset.

Proposition 18.2. The retracts of $\underset{\sim}{R}$ are the closed connected
subsets of $\underset{\sim}{R}$.

Theorem 143. Each nonempty closed subset of $\underset{\sim}{C}$ is a retract
of $\underset{\sim}{C}$.

Corollary 143.1. If Y is a compact metric space then there
exists a continuous surjection $f : \underset{\sim}{C} \to Y$.

Corollary 143.2. A Hausdorff space Y is compact and metriz-
able if and only if there exists a continuous surjection $f : \underset{\sim}{C} \to Y$.

Theorem 144. If X is a locally connected, compact metric
space and $\epsilon > 0$, then there exists $\delta > 0$ such that if a, b $\in X$
with $\rho(a, b) < \delta$, then there exists a mapping $f : [0, 1] \to X$
such that $f(0) = a$, $f(1) = b$, and diam $f([0, 1]) < \epsilon$.

Theorem 145. (Hahn-Mazurkiewicz.) A Hausdorff space X is
a Peano continuum if and only if there exists a continuous surjection $f : [0, 1] \to X$.

Definition. A space X is arcwise connected if, for each
a, b $\in X$, there exists an arc A such that $\{a, b\} \subset A \subset X$. If
$p \in X$ and if each neighborhood of p contains an arcwise connected neighborhood of p, then X is locally arcwise connected

<u>at</u> p. If X is locally arcwise connected at each of its elements
then X is <u>locally arcwise connected</u>.

Theorem 146. Local arcwise connectedness at an element
implies local connectedness at that element. A connected, locally arcwise connected space is arcwise connected.

Theorem 147. The product of a family of arcs is arcwise
connected, and consequently arcwise connectedness is preserved
by products. In particular, all cubes and Euclidean spaces are
arcwise connected. If $n > 0$ then S^n is arcwise connected.

Our next significant result asserts that a Peano continuum
is arcwise connected. To facilitate the proof we introduce the
following artificial concept. Let X be a given Peano continuum,
x and y elements of X, and $f : [0, 1] \to X$ a continuous surjection.
A subset F of $[0, 1]$ has <u>property</u> (X, f, x, y) if F is closed,
$\{x, y\} \subset f(F)$ and $f(a) = f(b)$ whenever $]a, b[$ is one of the
components of $[0, 1] - F$.

Proposition 18.3. If X is a Peano continuum, x and y are
elements of X, and $f : [0, 1] \to X$ is a continuous surjection,
then $[0, 1]$ contains a subset which is minimal relative to having
property (X, f, x, y).

Proposition 18.4. If X, x, y, and f satisfy the hypotheses
of Proposition 18.3. and if F is a subset of $[0, 1]$ which is
minimal relative to having property (X, f, x, y) then f(F) is
connected.

Theorem 148. (R. L. Moore.) A Peano continuum is arcwise
connected.

(Hint: If F satisfies Proposition 18.4, show that each
element of $f(F) - \{x, y\}$ cuts f(F).)

Corollary 148.1.   If X is an arcwise connected space, Y is
a Hausdorff space, and f : X → Y is a continuous surjection,
then Y is arcwise connected.

Theorem 149.   A locally connected, connected, complete
metric space is arcwise connected.

Corollary 149.1.   A locally connected, complete metric
space is locally arcwise connected.

There is another "more intuitive" proof of Theorem 148,
which is similar to the proof of Theorem 140.   If a and b are
elements of a Peano continuum X, one obtains a simple chain,
$\mathcal{C}_0$, of connected open sets from a to b, with $\text{diam}(C) < 2^0$ for
each $C \in \mathcal{C}_0$.   Obtain another simple chain $\mathcal{C}_1$, whose members have
diameter $< 2^{-1}$, and which "runs through" $\mathcal{C}_0$ without retracing
its steps at any stage.   Continuing this procedure with enough
care, the set $\bigcap_{n=0}^{\infty} \{\overline{\cup \mathcal{C}_n}\}$ will be an arc.

19

PARTIALLY ORDERED SPACES[1]

It has already been noted that (simply) ordered spaces constitute a useful and interesting class of topological spaces. They arose naturally from the study of $\underline{R}$, $\mathcal{O}(\Omega)$, etc. In this chapter we introduce and study a generalization of ordered spaces-- the so-called partially ordered spaces--which have applications to a wider class of objects.

Definition. A _partially ordered space_ is a triple $(X, \mathcal{J}, \Gamma)$ where $(X, \mathcal{J})$ is a topological space, (X, Γ) is a partially ordered set, and Γ is a closed subset of $X \times X$.

Remark. Where the context is free of ambiguity we will refer to "the partially ordered space X," suppressing the symbols $\mathcal{J}$ and Γ.

Notation. As noted in Chapter 0, we write $x \leq y$ as a synonym for $(x, y) \in \Gamma$. It is also helpful to introduce the following symbols in a partially ordered space X. If $x \in X$ then
$$\Gamma x = \{y \in X : (y, x) \in \Gamma\},$$
$$x\Gamma = \{y \in X : (x, y) \in \Gamma\};$$
and if $A \subset X$ then
$$\Gamma A = \cup \{\Gamma x : x \in A\},$$
$$A\Gamma = \cup \{x\Gamma : x \in A\}.$$

Examples.

(1) If X is a discrete space then X is a partially ordered space relative to any partial order on X.

(2)   Any Hausdorff space H is a partially ordered space
with respect to the trivial partial order $\Gamma = \{(x, x) : x \in H\}$.

(3)   The Euclidean space $\underset{\sim}{R}^n$ is a partially ordered space
with respect to $\Gamma = \{(x, y) \in \underset{\sim}{R}^n \times \underset{\sim}{R}^n : x_i \leq y_i$ for each $i = 1,$
..., $n\}$.

Proposition 19.1.   An ordered set with the order topology
is a partially ordered space. Every subspace of a partially
ordered space is a partially ordered space with respect to the
natural partial order it inherits.

Proposition 19.2.   If $\mathcal{X} = \{(X_\alpha, \Gamma_\alpha) : \alpha \in A\}$ is a family
of partially ordered spaces, then $X = \Pi\{X_\alpha\}$ is a partially ordered space with respect to the partial order
$$\Gamma = \{(x, y) \in X \times X : (x_\alpha, y_\alpha) \in \Gamma_\alpha \text{ for each } \alpha \in A\}.$$

Theorem 150.   If X is a partially ordered space and $x \in X$,
then the sets Γx and $x\Gamma$ are closed.

Theorem 151.   If X is a space endowed with a partial order
Γ then the following statements are equivalent.

(i)   X is a partially ordered space.

(ii)   If $(a, b) \in X \times X - \Gamma$ then there exist open neighborhoods U and V of a and b, respectively, such that $(U \times V) \cap \Gamma = \square$.

(iii)   If $(a, b) \in X \times X - \Gamma$ then there exist neighborhoods
M and N of a and b, respectively, such that $M \cap N = \square$, $M = M\Gamma$,
and $N = \Gamma N$.

Corollary 151.1.   Every partially ordered space is a Hausdorff space.

Theorem 152.   If K is a compact subset of a partially ordered space then ΓK and $K\Gamma$ are closed sets.

Theorem 153.   In a partially ordered space each maximal
chain is a closed subset.

Definition. An element p of a partially ordered set is maximal if pΓ = {p} and is minimal if Γp = {p}.

Theorem 154. A compact partially ordered space has at least one maximal element and at least one minimal element.

Definition. A partial order on a set S is dense provided, for each a ∈ S and b ∈ S such that a < b, there exists x ∈ S such that a < x < b.

Theorem 155. If C is a connected chain of a partially ordered space, then the partial order is dense on C. Conversely, if (X, Γ) is a compact partially ordered space and Γ is dense, then each maximal chain of X is connected.

Definition. A zero of a partially ordered set S is an element 0 such that 0Γ = S.

It is obvious that a partially ordered set can contain at most one zero.

Corollary 155.1. If (X, Γ) is a compact partially ordered space with zero, and if Γ is dense, then X is connected.

Corollary 155.2. If (X, Γ) is a compact, metrizable partially ordered space, and if Γ is dense, then each maximal chain of X is an arc.

Definition. Let X be a connected space and e ∈ X. Define ≤ on X by x ≤ y if and only if x = e, or x = y, or x separates e and y. Then ≤ is called the cutpoint partial order on X with basepoint e.

Example.
(4) If X = [0, 1] then the natural order is the cutpoint partial order with basepoint 0.

Theorem 156. If X is a connected space and e $\in$ X, then the cutpoint partial order with basepoint e is a partial order. Moreover, e is a zero and Γx is a chain for each x $\in$ X.

Theorem 157. If X is a locally connected continuum, then each cutpoint partial order on X is closed.

Definition. A tree is a continuum in which each two distinct elements are separated by some element.

Examples.

(5) [0, 1] is a tree.

(6) Let A_1, ..., A_n be arcs, say A_i = [a, b_i] where, if i $\neq$ j, then $A_i \cap A_j$ = {a}. Then $\cup_{i=1}^{n} \{A_i\}$ is a tree.

(7) In $\underset{\sim}{R}^2$ let A_{-2} = {(x, 0) : 0 $\leq$ x $\leq$ 1}, A_{-1} = {(0, y) : 0 $\leq$ y $\leq$ 1}, and for n = 0, 1, 2, ... let A_n = {(2^{-n}, y) : 0 $\leq$ y $\leq$ 1}. Then X = $\cup_{n=-2}^{\infty} \{A_n\}$ is not a tree. However, T = {(x, y) $\in$ X : y $\leq$ x} is a tree.

(8) A tree cannot contain a simple closed curve.

Theorem 158. If T is a tree, x $\in$ T, and V is a neighborhood of x, then there exists a neighborhood U of x such that U $\subset$ V and ∂U is finite.

Theorem 159. A tree is locally connected.

Theorem 160. Let X be a compact Hausdorff space. A necessary and sufficient condition that X be a tree is that X admit a partial order Γ such that

(i) (X, Γ) is a partially order space,

(ii) Γ is dense,

(iii) if x $\in$ X and y $\in$ X then Γx $\cap$ Γy is a nonempty chain, and

(iv) if x $\in$ X then xΓ - {x} is an open set.

Theorem 161. A metrizable continuum is a tree if and only if it is locally connected and contains no simple closed curve.

Definition. A space X has the fixed-point property if, for each mapping $f : X \to X$, there exists $x \in X$ such that $x = f(x)$. The element x is called a fixed point of f.

Examples.

(9) S^1 does not have the fixed-point property.

(10) If X has the fixed-point property, then X is connected.

Theorem 162. If X is a space with the fixed-point property and Y is a retract of X, then Y has the fixed-point property.

Theorem 163. A compact connected ordered space has the fixed-point property. In particular, [0, 1] has the fixed-point property.

Theorem 164. A tree has the fixed-point property.

(Hint: Give the tree T the cutpoint partial order and consider $P = \{x \in T : x \leq f(x)\}$.)

FOOTNOTE

[1] This chapter is independent of the remainder of the book and may be omitted.

20

THE BROUWER FIXED-POINT THEOREM

There seems to be no way to extend the rather simple order-theoretic proofs of Theorems 163 and 164 to a more general class of locally connected continua. More powerful tools are required, and this need motivates the following digression into combinatorial topology. For the present we confine our discussion to the space $\underset{\sim}{R}^2$.

A 0-<u>simplex</u> is an element of $\underset{\sim}{R}^2$. If v_0 and v_1 are distinct elements of $\underset{\sim}{R}^2$, then $[v_0, v_1]$ denotes the closed line segment joining v_0 and v_1. This segment is called a 1-<u>simplex</u>. If v_0, v_1, and v_2 are noncolinear elements of $\underset{\sim}{R}^2$, then $[v_0, v_1, v_2]$ is the union of all line segments joining elements of $[v_0, v_1] \cup [v_1, v_2] \cup [v_2, v_0]$. The set $[v_0, v_1, v_2]$ is called a 2-<u>simplex</u>. The three 1-simplexes $[v_0, v_1]$, $[v_1, v_2]$, and $[v_0, v_0]$ are the <u>edges</u> of $[v_0, v_1, v_2]$, and the three 0-simplexes v_0, v_1, and v_2 are the <u>vertices</u> of $[v_0, v_1, v_2]$.

If T^2 is a 2-simplex, then a <u>simplicial</u> <u>decomposition</u> of T^2 is a finite family $\mathscr{A} = \{T_1^2, \ldots, T_k^2\}$ of 2-simplexes such that $\cup \mathscr{A} = T^2$, and if $i \neq j$ then $T_i^2 \cap T_j^2$ is either empty, a common vertex, or a common edge of T_i^2 and T_j^2. (See Figure 3.)

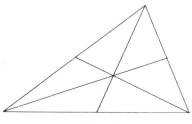

FIGURE 3

Proposition 20.1. If T^2 is a 2-simplex and $\epsilon > 0$, then T^2 admits a simplicial decomposition $\mathscr{A}$ such that $\text{diam}(T_j^2) < \epsilon$ for each $T_j^2 \in \mathscr{A}$.

We assume the geometric fact that an edge of a simplicial decomposition $\mathscr{A}$ of T^2 which lies in the boundary of T^2 is an edge of only one member of $\mathscr{A}$. Every other edge of $\mathscr{A}$ is a common edge of two members of $\mathscr{A}$.

Definition. If $T^2 = [v_0, v_1, v_2]$ is a 2-simplex and if $\mathscr{A}$ is a simplicial decomposition of T^2, let E denote the set of vertices of $\mathscr{A}$. A function $\varphi : E \to \{v_0, v_1, v_2\}$ is a Sperner function for $\mathscr{A}$ provided (1) $\varphi(v_i) = v_i$ for $i = 0, 1, 2$, and (2) if $e \in E \cap [v_i, v_j]$ then $\varphi(e) = v_i$ or $\varphi(e) = v_j$. If $[e, e']$ is an edge of $\mathscr{A}$ and $\varphi(\{e, e'\}) = \{v_0, v_1\}$ then $[e, e']$ is a φ-basic edge of $\mathscr{A}$. If $T_j^2 = [e, e', e''] \in \mathscr{A}$ and $\varphi(\{e, e', e''\}) = \{v_0, v_1, v_2\}$ then T_j^2 is a φ-proper member of $\mathscr{A}$.

Theorem 165. If T^2 is a 2-simplex, $\mathscr{A}$ is a simplicial decomposition of T^2, φ is a Sperner function for $\mathscr{A}$, and $T_j^2 \in \mathscr{A}$, then at most two of the edges of T_j^2 are φ-basic. Moreover, T_j^2 is φ-proper if and only if exactly one of its edges is φ-basic.

Theorem 166. (Sperner's lemma for n = 2.) If T^2 is a 2-simplex, $\mathscr{A}$ is a simplicial decomposition of T^2, and φ is a Sperner function for $\mathscr{A}$, then there is an odd number of φ-proper members of $\mathscr{A}$.

(Hint: First verify the result for n = 1, i. e., if $\mathscr{A}_1$ is a subdivision of $[0, 1]$ whose vertices are mapped to 0 and 1 with 0 and 1 fixed, then there is an edge $T_j^1 \in \mathscr{A}_1$ whose vertices are mapped onto $\{0, 1\}$. If a_j is the number of φ-proper edges of $T_j^2 \in \mathscr{A}$, then it suffices to show that Σa_j is odd.)

Theorem 167. Let $T^2 = [v_0, v_1, v_2]$ be a 2-simplex and

suppose F_0, F_1, and F_2 are closed subsets of T^2 such that $v_i \in F_i$, $[v_i, v_j] \subset F_i \cup F_j$ for all i and j, and $T^2 \subset F_0 \cup F_1 \cup F_2$. Then $F_0 \cap F_1 \cap F_2 \neq \Box$.

(Hint: Otherwise the sets $T^2 - F_i$ form an open cover of T^2. If $\mathscr{A}$ is a simplicial decomposition of T^2 whose members have small diameter, use Theorem 166 to show that there exists $T_j^2 \in \mathscr{A}$ meeting each F_i.)

Theorem 168.   A 2-simplex has the fixed-point property.

(Hint: Let $v_0 = (0, 0)$, $v_1 = (1, 0)$, $v_2 = (0, 1)$. If f : $T^2 \rightarrow T^2$ is a mapping, let $f(x) = f(x_1, x_2) = (x_1', x_2')$. Define $F_0 = \{x \in T^2 : x_1' + x_2' \geq x_1 + x_2\}$, $F_1 = \{x \in T^2 : x_1 \geq x_1'\}$, and $F_2 = \{x \in T^2 : x_2 \geq x_2'\}$.)

Theorem 168 is usually called the Brouwer fixed-point theorem for n = 2, while Theorem 163 includes the Brouwer fixed-point theorem for n = 1. The proof for the case n = 2 includes all the ingredients essential to the general case, and it is necessary only to extend the definitions to achieve this.

If v_0, ..., v_n are n + 1 elements of $\underset{\sim}{R}^n$, no k of which lie on the same (k - 2)-dimensional hyperplane[1], and if the (n - 1)-simplexes have been defined, then $T^n = [v_0, ..., v_n]$ is the union of all line segments in $\underset{\sim}{R}^n$ which join elements of the (n - 1)-simplexes $[v_{i_0}, ..., v_{i_{n-1}}]$. The set T^n is an n-simplex. A k-simplex $[v_{i_0}, ..., v_{i_k}]$ is a k-face of T^n. In this usage, a vertex of T^n is a 0-face of T^n.

A simplicial decomposition of the n-simplex T^n is a finite family $\mathscr{A} = \{T_1^n, ..., T_k^n\}$ of n-simplexes such that $T^n = \cup \mathscr{A}$ and $T_i^n \cap T_j^n$ is either empty or a common face of T_i^n and T_j^n.

We assume that if T^n is an n-simplex and $\epsilon > 0$, then T^n admits a simplicial decomposition whose members all have diameter less than ϵ. Moreover, we assume that an $(n - 1)$-face of the decomposition $\mathscr{d}$ is a face of exactly one member of $\mathscr{d}$ if and only if it lies on the boundary of T^n. Otherwise, it is a common face of two members of the decomposition.

If $\mathscr{d} = \{T_1^n, \ldots, T_k^n\}$ is a simplicial decomposition of the n-simplex T^n, let E denote the set of vertices of $\mathscr{d}$. A function $\varphi : E \to \{v_0, \ldots, v_n\}$ is a _Sperner_ _function_ for $\mathscr{d}$ if, whenever $e \in E$ and $e \in [v_{i_0}, \ldots, v_{i_k}]$, then $\varphi(e) \in \{v_{i_0}, \ldots, v_{i_k}\}$. An $(n - 1)$-face $[e_{i_0}, \ldots, e_{i_{n-1}}]$ of the decomposition is φ-_basic_ provided $\varphi(\{e_{i_0}, \ldots, e_{i_{n-1}}\}) = \{v_0, \ldots, v_{n-1}\}$. An element $T_i^n = [e_0, \ldots, e_n]$ of $\mathscr{d}$ is φ-_proper_ if $\varphi(\{e_0, \ldots, e_n\}) = \{v_0, \ldots, v_n\}$.

Theorem 169. (Sperner's Lemma.) If T^n is an n-simplex, $\mathscr{d}$ is a simplicial decomposition of T^n, and φ is a Sperner function for $\mathscr{d}$, then there is an odd number of φ-proper members of $\mathscr{d}$.

Theorem 170. (Brouwer.) An n-simplex has the fixed-point property.

Theorem 171. The set S^{n-1} is not a retract of the n-cell.

Theorem 172. Any cube has the fixed-point property.

FOOTNOTE

[1]That is, if $\lambda_1, \ldots, \lambda_k$ are real numbers then $\lambda_1 v_{i_1} + \lambda_2 v_{i_2} + \cdots + \lambda_k v_{i_k} = 0$ occurs only when $\lambda_1 = \lambda_2 = \cdots = \lambda_k = 0$.

Definition. Let X and Y be spaces. Two mappings f, g : X → Y are homotopic if there exists a mapping H : X × I → Y such that

$$H(x, 0) = f(x), \quad H(x, 1) = g(x),$$

for all x ∈ X. We say that H is a homotopy and write f ≅ g.

If H : X × I → Y is a homotopy, it is convenient to write $h_t(x) = H(x, t)$. Note that each h_t is a mapping, $h_0 = f$, and $h_1 = g$.

Proposition 21.1. All mappings from a space X into $\underset{\sim}{R}^n$ are homotopic.

Definition. A mapping is said to be inessential if it is homotopic to a constant mapping. If f is inessential, we write f ≅ 0.

Proposition 21.2. If X is a space, $f : X → S^n$ is a mapping, and f is not surjective, then f ≅ 0.

Proposition 21.3. Homotopy is an equivalence relation among the mappings from a space X into a space Y.

Proposition 21.4. If f_1, f_2 are mappings on a space X into a space Y, and if g_1, g_2 are mappings on a space Y into a space Z, such that $f_1 ≅ f_2$ and $g_1 ≅ g_2$, then $g_1 f_1 ≅ g_2 f_2$.

Definition. If H : X × I → X is a homotopy and if h_0 is

102

the identity, then H is a _deformation_. If H is a deformation
and if h_1 is a constant mapping, then H is a _contraction_ and X
is said to be _contractible_.

Proposition 21.5. The space $\underset{\sim}{R}^n$ is contractible.

Proposition 21.6. If $\mathfrak{X}$ is a family of contractible spaces,
then $\Pi\mathfrak{X}$ is contractible. In particular, any cube is contractible.

Proposition 21.7. A retract of a contractible space is
contractible.

Example.

(1) If X is any space then $Cn(X)$ is contractible.

Definition. If $H : X \times I \to X$ is a deformation and if h_1 is
a retraction of X onto Y, then H is a _deformation_ _retraction_
and Y is a _deformation_ _retract_ of X. If $h_t | Y$ is the identity
mapping for each $t \in I$, then Y is a _strong_ _deformation_ _retract_
of X.

Proposition 21.8. If X is a contractible space and $x \in X$,
then $\{x\}$ is a deformation retract of X.

Examples.

(2) It does not follow that if X is a contractible space
and $x \in X$, then $\{x\}$ is a strong deformation retract of X. Let
A_n denote the line segment joining $(0, 0)$ and $(1, 2^{-n})$ for
$n = 1, 2, \ldots$ and let A_0 denote the line segment joining $(0, 0)$
and $(1, 0)$. Let $x = (1, 0)$. (See Figure 4.)

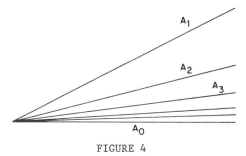

FIGURE 4

(3) The set S^n is a strong deformation retract of $\underset{\sim}{R}^{n+1} - \{0\}$.

Definition. Two spaces X and Y are homotopically equivalent if there exist mappings $f : X \to Y$ and $g : Y \to X$ such that gf and fg are homotopic to the identity mappings of X and Y, respectively. The mapping f is called a homotopy equivalence. If X and Y are homotopically equivalent, we write $X \cong Y$.'

Proposition 21.9. If Y is a deformation retract of the space X then $X \cong Y$.

Proposition 21.10. If X and Y are spaces, $X \cong Y$, and X is contractible, then Y is contractible.

Theorem 173. The space S^n is not contractible.

(Hint: Apply Theorem 171.)

Theorem 174. If $\underset{\sim}{R}^n$ and $\underset{\sim}{R}^m$ are homeomorphic then m = n.

In this chapter we will associate with every space X a group called the _fundamental_ _group_ of X. The motive for doing this is to translate topological questions about X into algebraic ones--hopefully, into questions easier to resolve. It is beyond the scope of this book to pursue this objective, but it is hoped that some sense of the flavor of the translation is transmitted.

Definition. A mapping $f : I \to X$, where X is a space, is called a _path_. If $x_0 = f(0) = f(1)$, then f is called a _loop_ _with_ _basepoint_ x_0.

If f and g are two paths in the space X and if $f(1) = g(0)$, then there is a _product_ _path_ $(g \circ f) : I \to X$ defined by

$$(g \circ f)(t) = \begin{cases} f(2t), & 0 \le t \le 1/2 \\ g(2t - 1), & 1/2 \le t \le 1. \end{cases}$$

With each path $f : I \to X$ there is associated an _inverse_ _path_ $\bar{f} : I \to X$ defined by

$$\bar{f}(t) = f(1 - t).$$

Proposition 22.1. Path multiplication is well defined and associative. That is, if f, g, and h are paths in X such that $f(1) = g(0)$ and $g(1) = h(0)$, then $g \circ f$ and $h \circ g$ are paths and $h \circ (g \circ f) = (h \circ g) \circ f$. Moreover, $\overline{g \circ f} = \bar{f} \circ \bar{g}$ and $\overline{\bar{f}} = f$.

Definition. Let f and g be paths in X such that $f(0) = g(0)$ and $f(1) = g(1)$. If f and g are homotopic under a homotopy

105

H, and if H(0, t) = f(0) = g(0) and H(1, t) = f(1) = g(1) for
all t ∈ I, then f and g are said to be homotopic with fixed endpoints.

Warning. Hereafter, if f and g are paths in a space X, we
write f ≅ g to mean that f and g are homotopic with fixed endpoints.

Proposition 22.2. Homotopy of paths with fixed endpoints
is an equivalence relation.

Definition. The path e : I → X defined by e(t) = x_0, for
all t ∈ I, is called the constant path at x .
                                                                 0

Proposition 22.3. If f : I → X is a path, e_0 is the constant path at f(0), and e_1 is the constant path at f(1), then
$(e_1 \circ f \circ e_0) \cong (e_1 \circ f) \cong (f \circ e_0) \cong f$.

Notation. If X is a space and x_0 ∈ X, then $\Omega(X, x_0)$ denotes
the set of loops in X with basepoint x_0.

Remark. If f, g ∈ $\Omega(X, x_0)$ then it is clear that f ∘ g is
defined and is a member of $\Omega(X, x_0)$.

Notation. If X is a space, x_0 ∈ X, and f ∈ $\Omega(X, x_0)$, then
[f] denotes the equivalence class of f in the set $\Omega(X, x_0)$. We
write $\pi_1(X, x_0)$ to denote the set of equivalence classes of
$\Omega(X, x_0)$.

Theorem 175. If X is a space and x_0 ∈ X, then $\pi_1(X, x_0)$
is a group with respect to the operation [f] ∘ [g] = [f ∘ g].
Moreover, [e] is the identity element of $\pi_1(X, x_0)$, and if
f ∈ $\Omega(X, x_0)$ then $[f]^{-1} = [\bar{f}]$ and $[f] \circ [f]^{-1} = [e]$.

Definition. The group $\pi_1(X, x_0)$ is the fundamental group
of the space X with basepoint x_0.

Theorem 176. Let X be a space and suppose p : I → X is a path with $x_0 = p(0)$ and $x_1 = p(1)$. For each loop $f \in \Omega(X, x_0)$, define

$$p_*([f]) = [p \circ f \circ \bar{p}].$$

Then p_* is an isomorphism of $\pi_1(X, x_0)$ onto $\pi_1(X, x_1)$. If q is a path in X and $p \cong q$, then $p_* = q_*$. If r is a path in X such that $p(1) = r(0)$ then $r_* p_* = (r \circ p)_*$.

Corollary 176.1. If X is an arcwise connected space, then the fundamental group of X is independent of the basepoint. That is, if x_0 and x_1 are elements of X then $\pi_1(X, x_0) \cong \pi_1(X, x_1)$.

Notation. If X is an arcwise connected space, we write $\pi_1(X)$ for the fundamental group of X.

Theorem 177. If X and Y are spaces, $x_0 \in X$, and f : X → Y is a mapping, let $y_0 = f(x_0)$. For each $w \in \Omega(X, x_0)$ define $f_*([w]) = [fw]$. Then $f_* : \pi_1(X, x_0) \to \pi_1(Y, y_0)$ is a homomorphism. If Z is a space and g : Y → Z is a mapping, then $(gf)_* = g_* f_*$. Finally, if f is a homeomorphism onto Y, then f_* is an isomorphism onto $\pi_1(Y, y_0)$.

Examples.
(1) Every contractible space has a trivial fundamental group.
(2) If X and Y are spaces and $X \cong Y$, then $\pi_1(X, x_0) \cong \pi_1(Y, y_0)$, where $x_0 \in X$ and y_0 is the image of x_0 under the homotopy equivalence.

It follows from Example 1 that all Euclidean spaces have trivial fundamental groups. We shall prove next that S^1 does not have a trivial fundamental group. It is helpful here to recall that $\underline{R}$ is a group under addition and S^1 is a group under multiplication of complex numbers.

Proposition 22.4. Define $\varphi : \underline{R} \to S^1$ by $\varphi(t) = e^{2\pi i t}$. Then φ is an open mapping and a homomorphism. Further, if $f : I \to S^1$ is a path with $f(0) = 1$, then there is a unique path $f' : I \to \underline{R}$ such that $f'(0) = 0$ and $\varphi f' = f$.

Proposition 22.5. If $H : I \times I \to S^1$ is a homotopy of paths with fixed endpoints, and if $H(0, 0) = 1$, then there is a unique homotopy of paths with fixed endpoints, say $H' : I \times I \to \underline{R}$, such that $H'(0, 0) = 0$ and $\varphi H' = H$.

Theorem 178. $\pi_1(S^1) \cong \underline{Z}$.

Theorem 179. If X and Y are spaces, $x_0 \in X$, and $y_0 \in Y$, then $\pi_1(X \times Y, (x_0, y_0)) \cong \pi_1(X, x_0) \times \pi_1(Y, y_0)$.

Corollary 179.1. $\pi_1(S^1 \times S^1) \cong \underline{Z} \times \underline{Z}$.

Theorem 180. The group $\pi_1(S^n)$ is trivial if $n \geq 2$.

SUBJECT INDEX